Praise for Wild

'Marries words and images to create a special echo of
this country's rich past'
The Times

'Across seven themed chapters the *Storyland* author
presents an inspiring excavation of the British
countryside through diverse medieval texts'
Waterstones (Best History Books of 2022)

'Jeffs teases out nuance, divining moral and metaphorical
meaning from each story, and questions ways that this
living history of Britain impacts upon our present-day
understanding of landscape. The writing throughout
is celebratory and evocative'
Art Quarterly

'Jeffs has a gift for breathing new life into ancient stories
through her lyrical writing, deep research and evocative
woodcuts . . . Reading *Wild* feels like being led by the
hand through a gnarled, old growth forest, along empty
shoreflats, and along the edge of windswept cliffs . . .
It's a jewel of a book'
Natalie Lawrence (co-author of
Planta Sapiens: Unmasking Plant Intelligence)

Also by Amy Jeffs

STORYLAND

Wild

Tales from Early Medieval Britain

AMY JEFFS

riverrun

First published in Great Britain in 2022 by riverrun
This paperback edition published in 2023 by

riverrun

An imprint of

Quercus Editions Ltd
Carmelite House
50 Victoria Embankment
London EC4Y 0DZ

An Hachette UK company

A CIP catalogue record for this book is available
from the British Library

Paperback 978 1 52942 426 3
Ebook ISBN 978 1 52942 424 9

10 9 8 7 6 5 4 3 2 1

Designed and typeset by EM&EN
Printed and bound in Italy by L.E.G.O. S.p.A.

Papers used by Quercus are from well-managed forests
and other responsible sources.

For Will

Sum mæg . . .

sele asettan,   con he sidne ræced

fæste gefegan   wiþ færdryrum.

Another has the skill . . .

to build a hall; he knows how to truss

the spacious building, against collapse.

(The Exeter Book, folios 78v–8ov)

Contents

Contents

Wild

Prologue: Wayless

In museums, libraries and the landscape, a memory remains of a wilderness of unquiet graves, riddling marshes and storm-beaten cliffs. The stories to come and the commentaries that follow them were inspired by these memories, found in cultural artefacts whose words and images shed light on the idea of the wild in early medieval Britain. I have sought to capture flashes of the cruel garnet eyes that wink from the treasures of the Sutton Hoo ship burial, and the beautiful, haunting atmosphere of the Old English elegies, Welsh *englynion* and Irish *immrama*. These survivals – whether poetic, artistic, carved from whale's bone or cast in solid gold – were forged by cultures with a world view very different from our own. My aim has been to evoke and contextualise an ancient imaginative landscape. Using as its pole-star the mesmerising corpus of Old English elegies in the Exeter Book, this book explores texts translated from Old English, Medieval Welsh, Old Irish and Insular Latin, alongside sculpture and illuminated manuscripts from the same age.

Focusing on this theme, the commentaries by which the stories are followed serve also to introduce the period *circa* 600–1000, an age of migration, conversion, and belief in monsters, demons, angels and omens in the sky. This was an age in which the Celtic Britons were consolidating power in the West, while Germanic tribes were settling in the East, soon to call themselves the English. In the North, conquering Irish kingdoms vied with the Picts, and Norse aggression threatened the coast and outlying islands. All the while, the population was experiencing a long spell of cold and stormy weather.

This book explores the traditions of cultures, variously co-existing, conflicting and cross-fertilising, that were transformed by the importation of new ideas, media, materials and styles by Christian missionaries from Rome and Ireland. I have illustrated each chapter with wood engravings, ink impressions of lines incised in close-grained timber, which are here printed to scale. They are exchanged, in the audiobook edition of this text (the form in which most medieval people would have consumed literature), for songs.

But why, of all the many aspects of these survivals that deserve our attention, choose the wilderness? I did so because the idea of the 'wild' is enjoying a renaissance, as we learn more about what we need to do to foster biodiversity, capture carbon and safeguard our environment. We live in an age in which the restoration of land to a wild state is of crucial importance and a source of burgeoning fascination. We are also realising the vigour of nature in recolonising landscapes thought to be waste: landscapes left for dead by war, industry or pollution. We have a new occasion to wonder at nature's ability to come back to life, and we have the past to explore for yet more reasons to be amazed. This book is inspired by a past landscape dominated by wild spaces and a world view that looked for lessons in every leaf, swarm and downpour.

Bleak and chilly as the early medieval portrayal of the wild often is, the philosophies that lie beneath send up rays of brilliant hope. The ice-encrusted, storm-swept, eel-infested, midnight-sun-illuminated wilderness of literature in Old English, Insular Latin and Middle Welsh, lends drama to the articulation of philosophies inherited from the works of Classical thinkers, the Bible, and Germanic and Celtic pre-Christian traditions. The messages that shine through are timeless in their comfort: this too shall pass, we are part of something beautiful, creation is full of wisdom.

I hope the stories' accessibility will encourage the greatest number of readers towards the wonders of the primary sources, while keeping those sources alive in our culture by means of creative interpretation. What is more, most of the chosen poems share an enticing narrative incompleteness to which I wanted to respond. They often provide tantalising allusions to stories and situations, perhaps even to solutions of the kind possessed by riddles, that have been forgotten. I was itching to invent some of the background drama.

As for the reflections that follow the stories, they will return time and again to a manuscript called the Exeter Book. Its wood and leather binding encloses some of the most important poems in Old English, the language spoken and written down by the Germanic migrants to Britain. Their language, of which there were many dialects, is more like modern Dutch or German than the English of today. When French joined the vernaculars of England after the Norman Conquest, English underwent a transformation, becoming, by around the twelfth century, what we call Middle English and by the time of Shakespeare, modern.

The Old English poems in the Exeter Book were written down in around 970 and together form one of only four surviving major anthologies of Old English poetry. If the manuscript had not been left to Exeter Cathedral by Leofric, first Bishop of Exeter, upon his death in 1072, and remained protected there ever since, we might have lost a precious record of the humour and emotional subtlety of pre-Conquest culture.

The Exeter Book has one hundred and twenty-three folios, or leaves, of high quality animal skin parchment, inscribed in a murmuration of Old English letters. Many of these preserve the entertaining, wildly imaginative and sometimes obscene Old English riddles. Other poems in the Exeter Book include the adventures of fenland hermit St Guthlac and verses inspired by *The Physiologus*, a text from the second century CE, originally in Greek, describing animals, birds, mythical beasts and the moral lessons they provide.

But some of the Exeter Book's most striking poems, at least to modern ears, are the Old English 'elegies'. They live among the riddles, their composition dated to as early as the eighth century, and, like most other Old English poems, use stress and alliteration rather than rhyme. Whether the elegies are riddles themselves is a delightful if unsolvable question. What makes them relevant here is their story-laden evocation of a north-western European landscape, its animals, weather and seasons, as well as the intriguing psychologies of their narrators and allusion to fascinating backstories which may be lost or may never have existed at all.

Yet, while the Exeter Book poems, in the Germanic tongue, served as a polestar in the making of this book, I have sought to demonstrate their connection and debt to the Celtic world. Britain has always been a mixture of cultures, ethnicities and religions, and though I have kept a narrow scope for the sake of accessibility and according to the field of my own expertise, this book could be written a hundred times over with just a slight movement of the magnifying glass over the surface of the map.

The illustrations are another response to the original poems and artefacts. They are wood engravings (rather than woodcuts, which is a different technique).

Wood engraving is a printmaking method whereby the maker incises minute lines and dots into the end-grain of a dense, slow-grown timber like box or lemonwood. When the engraved block is covered with ink and the image transferred to paper, the incised lines and dots show up white. I chose this medium because I love how it looks. The black ink of the printed image seems to grow from the black ink of the printed text. I also love the confines in which it compels the artist to work. Like the interlace found on medieval artworks or the tightly wrought lines of Old English and Welsh *englynion* verses, it offers freedom within form. My boundaries for the pictures in this book were 75 × 100 mm and monochrome. If you are listening to this book, then I have sought to achieve a similar effect with the songs: voice out of voice, melding the traditional and contemporary. For those eager to discover the sources in greater depth, the end of this book offers a selection of the Exeter Book poems newly translated by George Younge, lecturer in Medieval Literature at the University of York. More resources may be found beyond that, in the Further Reading section. I am indebted to all those scholars – Elaine Treharne, Jenny Rowland and more – who have translated these texts to Modern English.

In years gone by, peat diggers at the Avalon Marshes (the haunt of the starlings described in Chapter Seven) discovered remnants of numerous prehistoric tracks through the wetland. One of these paths, the so-called Sweet Track, was made in the early Neolithic period out of X-shaped pairs of timbers driven into the ground, with planks fixed to the upper V to form bridges over the water.

Walking a reconstruction of this path, snaking over the temperate mangrove of scrubby oaks and birches, demonstrated to me something that had been knocking at the door of my consciousness for much of my travel for this book. For as long as we humans have wandered the earth, wild places have required us to build paths to gain access, whether physically or imaginatively. Sometimes it can be easier to pretend wild places don't exist or obliterate them altogether, but in the long term, what a mistake that proves to be. To access the wild by what we have made or dreamed of, is to realise we are part of it after all. We have a profound affinity with the wild.

Wilderness

Middle Welsh

annialwch: desert, wilderness, solitude.

atref: without settlement.

Old English

wēsten: related to the term 'wasteland': uncultivated land.

wēglæst: a way-less place.

Latin

avium: a place without paths.

solitudo: loneliness, wilderness.

Chapter One

Earth

The Lament of Hos

Cold it is, cold and so close that I can feel my neighbours against me, their beards and bones rotting like stacks of winter branches. I hear the voices of elves, goblins and old gods that haunt these unhallowed halls. They whisper that I am friendless: that my old companions are dead, that my love has left me forever, that I must hope without hope until I am no more than an ache in the air. And always it is dark but for that one ray of light, now bright, now dim, which spears through the gloom. I have pressed my eye to the hole through which it passes and seen, behind the boughs of an oak tree, the sun drag – so slowly it must be yearning to die – from dark to dark, until all at once it is done and another day has passed. And another day has passed in which my beloved has not come for me. But he will. He must. He told me to wait. Why would he leave me here among the corpses with no news? In this ancient earth-hall, I am all longing.

The sunlight is gone. The hood of the night promises me protection. If only I could escape and find him for myself. If only I could –

I work at the hole with my nails and teeth, with the iron file of my will, despite the words of the demons that throng behind me. I do not know if I have grown thin or if my work has wrought some change on the stone, but finger by finger – by elbow, shoulder and spine – I work my way to the air.

Lying on the leaf mould, feeling the dark wind on my head after the long, damp stillness, makes me weep for pleasure. Lifting myself, I scoop up the leaves, young in their decay, and press them to my face. They smell of life, of change, of the joyful arc of birth to death to which I no longer belong. Out here there are no voices but those of birds, and there are no shadows but those cast by the moonlight through the branches of the tree. I raise my head and look into the canopy. A thought passes through my mind like the shadow of a crow.

There were no trees here then.

I have been on this ground before; the thought excites me. I rise, for I remember the path, though it has since been lost to fallen leaves. My feet carry me back through the memories, through the forest that has grown since the day I first came here, across a hard grey river, a field, a band of aspens blowing moonlit, where once there were only reeds.

And then I am at the high place where the hall used to stand. The village has gone and not a footprint of what was remains, not a woven wall or post. New buildings, made of sharp stones, stand here now. Only the undulation of the ground is familiar. I move till I feel myself near where he met me on that warm night. There had been dancing. I had dressed, along with a few friends I had known since childhood, in the old costumes. Mine had a beast's head and a snake coiled around its snout. I carried a leafy branch. We danced in the hall, and the warriors laughed and stamped their feet to the music of the lyre and the rhythm of our steps. I could see him watching me. There was mead to go around that night, and after the dance I had met him in the willow bed behind the hall. He had lifted the headdress from my shoulders, behind the whispering reeds, and kissed me. He tasted of salt and honey. It had been bliss to touch at last after so long resisting, after so much had been promised in the exchange of glances. I am there again now, kneeling on the earth, in the pounding heat of it, the smell of moss and mead in my nostrils. And I remember how we promised each other we would be together. That was what he promised me.

'Bring your horse to the edge of the forest. Meet me there at dawn, Hos. We will run away. I love you.'

'I love you too, Ertae.'

When dawn came, I went to the margin of the trees and stood there with my horse, Biter, the one that no one else would have, but who was gentle in my care. I waited for Ertae but there was no glimpse of him between the branches, no snap of twigs to betray his approach. No. Instead, there, I saw the warriors, who were not laughing now. They moved stealthily through the branches. They seized and struck me, their breath all drink and eels. They called me mare. They called me bitch. They slew Biter, that innocent, untamed beast, and they punished me for my crime according to their own laws.

A black dog is barking at me from one of the windows, but I am no more than the memory of a wound. And now the sky bleaches at its eastern edge and I am travelling back past the buildings, through the brightening aspens, over the field and grey river to the forest, the leaf mould and the only place I will find rest, though I hate so much to return.

I remember now how they took me to the lord and thence to the barrow: a resting place of some ancient king and later the grave of criminals. The warriors made me kneel once more. The lord stood behind me, his teeth like splintered bone, a broadsword in his hand.

As the light strengthens, I sink into my earthen dugout, my narrow grave, the others pressing in: skeletons all, some maimed, some with malice still throbbing in their ribs. And I am one of them, the condemned. And though I know I am dead, I feel the ache of myself changing in the earth-grey gloom. And all at once I am not longing but fury. Where was Ertae when I was ready with my horse? Why did he not come? Who told the warriors where I would be waiting?

I lift my fingers to the back of my skull and feel the hair cropped by the blow of a blade. I touch a wound still weeping, deeper than my life allowed. And I remember kneeling with my hands tied before me, waiting for the blow to fall and the agony when it did. I remember the knowledge that nothing would ever again be well. And now I recall that I have made this journey every sunrise for a thousand years. Ertae let them kill me. He let them bury me. He let worms devour my corpse. And as the cursed mud of the scraped-away earth clings to my bones, I know one thing; because of him, I was executed and buried among the damned. As if paralysed on the sting of dawn, my last thought becomes a curse.

Ancient is this earth-hall and deadly to those who would enter. To me he is every living man, and I am nothing but hate.

The mystery of the Old English poem *The Wife's Lament* has long occupied scholars. Its narrator seems to be a woman, whose 'lord' has made her wait in an underground prison: an earth-cave or earth-hall beneath an oak tree. This she does, as the sun edges through the sky and brambles tangle overhead, shaded by encircling hills. All her friends are dead, she tells us. She does not give her name or the name of her lord, but in the end she describes him tormented, exiled and wandering. She expresses her sad fate in a final cry, 'Woe to those who must wait in longing!' Why is the narrator of the poem trapped underground? Why can't she leave? Why are her companions dead? Its lines, of which I here offer a few, newly translated by George Younge are haunting:

> A man (who else) made this canopied clearing
> my haunt: an earthen hollow at the heel of an oak.
> Time's old in this soil-hall, makes me lost with longing.
> Sunless fissures, looming hills,
> brooding earthworks smothered by briars:
> a place I call Sorrow. Often it seems
> like I'm roughly restrained by my man
> being gone. Elsewhere on earth
> friends live their lives, make the most of their beds,
> while I pace alone in a different dawn,
> circling the chamber at the heel of the oak.
> It's there that I sit all the summer-long day,
> It's there I lament all the losses I've made
> on the highways of hate. And so it goes,
> and always will: no rest from my raging heart,
> no rest from life's brutal longing.

Here, the earth-wild has dark associations. To an early medieval Christian, it parenthesised the body: the substance from which it was made and to which it would return, heavy with the threat of hell and hell's malevolent spirits. In another poem from Exeter Book (described in the introduction), Soul and Body II, the soul calls the body 'worm's meat', 'a semblance of clay', 'a foul thing of earth'. The soul accuses the body of holding it 'captive in hellish torments'.

Indeed, evocations of the underground pervade the Exeter Book. The earth is the domain of the dead, a realm of dangerous forces and strange, out-of-sight happenings on parchment as much as in real life. I experienced this for myself one moonlit January night, when caver Dan Matthews led me to one of the many cavities that snake through south-west England's Mendip Hills, not far from Exeter.

We crunched up a hillside covered in tangled haw-thorn trees and small oaks decorated with trembling ferns. Everywhere, rock formations pierced the soil, and soon we came to one with a dark opening, like the blow-hole of a whale in the hill's curved back. With the confidence of one who explores derelict stone mines for fun, Dan lowered himself out of sight.

Joining him in the entrance of the cave, I found

myself in a humid, still space quite different from the one outside. There were remnants of a fire on the ground: terrible for the bats, Dan tells me, who hibernate, dangling from the flowstone, but are driven out by smoke. Victorian visitors had broken off what there had once been of stalactites and stalagmites in that first cavern, but evidence of human activity lessened, the deeper we went.

One of the most compelling ideas held about the universe in the Middle Ages, was that it directly reflected the human body. *Man as microcosm.* I pondered this as we progressed. Using my head-torch, I observed the smooth, undulating space. I could see flowstone, glistening calcium deposits, looking like networks of veins. Where they congregated on the vertical faces, they put me in mind of clusters of wet sinew. We came to a steep tunnel and I slid down it, using my feet as brakes. In this damp, steep tube, it was as if the earth were swallowing me whole.

The channels in which I was lying were formed long ago by rushing, eddying water, looking for ways through the rock. The smooth recesses left behind, with their corporeal wetness and shapes, were like the body's own paths: vein, gullet, sinus.

The body, according to early medieval philosophers who inherited Classical lore, was in a state of constant imbalance. Its humours – blood, phlegm, black bile and yellow bile – were governed by the four equally restive elements of air, water, earth and fire. The narrator of one Old English riddle in the Exeter Book describes being forced underground, weighed down by the earth, constrained in the darkness by huge forces. Without any means of escape, it shudders and quakes, until far, far above, palaces and churches are shaken at their roots.

If you had asked an educated Old English speaker like Bede (died 735, also known as 'the Venerable Bede') what the riddle meant, he might have taken you to one of the great wooden book chests at the library in Monkwearmouth Jarrow, the monastery which had been his home since he was seven years old. With practised hands he might have lifted out a weighty manuscript of his own treatise *On the Nature of Things* and turned to the chapter entitled 'Earthquake'. The earth, he would inform you, has 'sponge-like innards', containing pockets of belching wind that 'with a terrifying roar and labouring to escape' seeks 'to discharge itself by shaking open a gap. Hence hollows in the earth are associated with these quakes.' Earthquakes, he might have said, pointing to the inky page, occur when 'wind is hidden in the veins of the earth'. Bede would have enlightened you that the solution to the riddle was 'wind', because subterranean wind, in wanting to return to the sky, fought to escape the earth and caused earthquakes.

The earth was riven with caves, swilling with underground lakes and rivers, and roaring with subterranean gales. It was the realm of Erebus and Tartarus: deep, malevolent places associated with the torments of hell. According to Isidore of Seville's *Etymologies* – an early seventh-century encyclopaedia widely read in medieval Europe – Tartarus was a cavity deep in the centre of the globe that derived its name from the Greek word for 'disturbance, upheaval or shivering' caused by being numb with cold. Tartarus was without light and sunshine, a place of perpetual numbness. 'Indeed,' writes Isidore, 'in that place is "weeping and gnashing of teeth" (Matthew 8: 12)'.

Our journey through the cave took some fifteen minutes and all too soon the tunnel began to ascend. The steep climb out of the cave took me past hibernating lesser horseshoe bats, whose whiskers poked out from between enveloping wings and whose minute, eyelash toes somehow found purchase on the stone. When we had emerged and were back in the forest, my husband greeted us; he hadn't been able to come too because he was holding our baby daughter. I took her, Dan led him back to the entrance and the sound of their conversation – about trance music and mining – faded to silence.

Cradling a baby alone in a cave entrance, in a cold, moonlit wood, was eerie enough, but it was also strangely reminiscent of The Wife's Lament. Archaeologist Sarah Semple had suggested that the prison of the exiled woman was intended to be understood as a prehistoric barrow. Her account of the early medieval idea of this curious category of subterranean space – man-made, ancient, often on the wild edges of human-occupied territories – reveals a litany of macabre superstitions.

A week after my visit to the cave, I took myself to a prehistoric barrow, wanting to see it through medieval eyes, as I had the cave. As I navigated the freezing fog, white in the sunrise, the stems of winter hemlock rose up like the arms of the undead. Mine were not the first feet to tramp these fields up to the structure we now call Stoney Littleton Long Barrow. It is some 5,500 years old and, before being filled in, was in use as a burial chamber for around two hundred years. Skeletal and cremated remains of numerous Bronze Age women, children and men were found tucked into its chambers when the hollow barrow was excavated in the early nineteenth century. For much of its history, however, it has been a rise or tumulus in the landscape of the kind seen all over Britain, its contents a mystery. It is the sort of barrow that would have been found on coastlines and territory boundaries by pagan Germanic tribes migrating from the Continent. There is some evidence that they built shrines on these already ancient tumps, as well as adding their own barrows to the landscape. With Christian conversion from the end of the sixth century, however, their practice took on a more chilling hue.

I chose Stoney Littleton because it's possible to get inside. The prospect of crawling into a dark cavity in which heaped human remains reposed, silent and sightless, for thousands of years, holds a morbid appeal. These were sites touched by the threat of the suffocating grave as well as spiritual malevolence (there is no divide between the natural and supernatural, the normal and paranormal, here).

After the conversion of the English to Christianity from the late sixth century, evidence begins to emerge of a period of intense superstition around these features of the landscape. Sarah Semple cites one harrowing discovery: a female burial from the period in question at the prehistoric barrow of Walkington Wold. The woman was thirty-eight to forty-five years old, buried in the flex position (with her knees up to her chin) and bore signs of having been executed from behind with a weapon such as an axe or broadsword. Not only that, but she was one of fifteen other bodies, all victims of execution. Apparently the prehistoric barrow, already ancient by the early medieval period, served as graveyard for the outcast dead. Andrew Reynolds' work on 'deviant' burials has shown that prehistoric barrows were often used in post-conversion, pre-Conquest England as execution cemeteries. They are frequently found on medieval territory boundaries: liminal places like crossroads that belong to no one; wild places away from the bosom of community. What is more, the early medieval skeletons within them show signs of violence or trauma, including decapitation, tied hands, feet and face-down (prone) burial, and perhaps even cadaveric spasm, a consequence of death in a state of extreme tension.

In some cases, fear of the dead may be indicated by the presence of stones weighing on the corpse, as in a double grave of an adult and child in Carlton Colville, wherein quern stones were laid over the adult's head. Quern stones were rocks the size of bar-bell weights, designed to grind materials like grain and used, on occasion, to keep the dead from walking.

To add context to Reynolds' archaeological findings about barrows as execution cemeteries, Semple provides haunting clues from literature. At the end of *Beowulf*, a dragon occupies a treasure-filled barrow. Likewise, two poems in the Exeter Book concerning the heroic deeds of a saint called Guthlac (died 715), tell the story of how the eponymous saint sought out a solitary existence in the wilderness of the East Anglian Fens and took for his abode a lonely hill or barrow, the only feature in an otherwise featureless wasteland. In the first poem *Guthlac A*, we learn, 'for *wlence on westenne / beorgas bræce*' ('for the sake of bravado in the wilderness, he violated the hills'). Guthlac did this for a reason. The poem tells us that it offered temporary respite to evil spirits and tormented souls, who were otherwise condemned to endless wandering. Guthlac, having woken them from their slumber and determined to make the hill his home, must exorcise the demons.

Semple offers place-names as further evidence for the imagined connection between barrows and malevolent powers. Words for barrow include: *beorg*, *hlæwe* and *howe*. These are coupled with words for devil (*scucca*), Woden (*Grim* or *Wodnes*) and elves (*elues*) in Shuckburgh, Shucklow, Grimshoe and Ailey Hill (formerly *Elueshou*). This, she elaborates, may explain the use of prehistoric barrows as execution cemeteries. Perhaps it was believed that the condemned soul would be tormented by devils.

Some parallels may exist here with pre-Christian Celtic beliefs surrounding prehistoric barrows. For instance, manuscripts such as *The Book of the Dun Cow* and *The Yellow Book of Lecan*, both dated to well into the post-conversion age, give the megalithic passage barrow Brú na Boínne as the site of numerous encounters between the old gods and legendary humans. Similarly, the Gaelic term *sídhe* refers to earth mounds that are the homes of the supernatural *Aos sí* ('people of the mounds'). Evidently, prehistoric barrows and ring forts have long had the power to fascinate.

My numb feet reached the last stile in the ascent to Stoney Littleton Long Barrow. It was freezing cold and ropes of icy cobwebs fettered the old timber before a stretch of scrubland between the pasture of the farm and the mown enclosure occupied by the monument. And then I was approaching the entrance, eager to discover what lay within. Slabs of stone flanked the doorway, one bearing an ammonite impression wider than my hand. Illuminated by the rising winter sun, the first few feet of drystone passageway were visible, but the deeper recesses were dark. I didn't wait. I stooped and went inside.

Drawing on the evidence of execution cemeteries, place-names and texts like *Guthlac A*, Semple suggests that the narrator of *The Wife's Lament* is the soul of an executed woman, trapped in a barrow by its resident hostile spirits. She goes on to draw a comparison with a fascinating, dismal scene carved on an object that was probably made in the eighth century, around the time the poem was composed: the Franks Casket.

The casket, made out of whale's bone, is named after Augustus Franks, who acquired it for the British Museum. He bought it from a Parisian antique shop, which had acquired it, via a dealer, from a French family in Auzon. They had been using it as a sewing box. Narrative scenes from Germanic, biblical and Classical sources fill every face. The subject of the right-hand panel, which concerns us here, is as yet unidentified.

It shows a figure seated on a stump or small hillock. The figure has hoofed feet and wears a tunic and cloak. The head appears to be that of a cow, horse or dog, and a snake coils around its snout. The figure looks as though it could be wearing a headdress of the kind worn today by folk mummers or else representative of the kind of shapeshifting found in the Norse myths. The beast-headed figure faces a warrior. Behind the warrior are a horse and a bird. Around them runes spell out the Old English words 'rush', 'biter' and 'wood'. Next comes an image of a hooded figure with a stick and a chalice, standing over a shrouded corpse in what may be a pyre or a barrow. Finally, a figure is shown being arrested by two others in hoods. So far, so utterly enigmatic.

An Old English border inscription in runic characters sheds a little more light on the scene. Runes are an alphabet (not a language) used by Germanic communities on either side of the North Sea. It was not used like the Roman alphabet, for administration and government. Rather, it is often encrypted and hard to decipher. The Franks Casket inscription reads something like 'Here Hos sits on the sorrow-mound; she suffers distress in that Ertae had decreed for her a wretched den of sorrows and torments of mind'. Here again is a tale of a woman confined to a mound and beset by mental anguish. If The Wife's Lament was intended to remind readers of a widely known story, is this the same story? Are Hos and Ertae the names of its lost protagonists?

I tend to think the mystery is sufficient. All art is mysterious on some level. However, fiction can take flight with theories that may never be proven in scholarship. I have offered a story inspired by the mystery of the Franks Casket and *The Wife's Lament*, as well as the presence of victims of execution in prehistoric barrows. You can't help but wonder . . . were some of them murderers? Were some of them witches? Perhaps some of them had simply loved the wrong person. For this, they had been buried at the edge of things, in a place steeped in danger. Like wind, the soul could be ensnared underground and, like the wind, it did not rest easy. For the narrator of *The Wife's Lament*, morning brings 'uhtcære' (anxieties at dawn). This juncture is time's equivalent to the landscape's contested borderlands.

Entering Stoney Littleton Long Barrow was a relief. Outside was hoar frost. Inside was so warm that water dripped from the ceiling. I had to crouch down as I crept deeper into the passageway and was almost kneeling by the time I reached the first chambers.

I could see fossils glinting from the stones about me as I edged my way through the dark. After a minute or two I was at the very end of the main passage, longer chambers opening up either side of me. I turned to look back towards the light. It was only now that I realised the distant entrance to the barrow framed the sunrise; at the darkest time of the year, the occupants received light from the earliest possible moment. I thought of the narrator of *The Wife's Lament*, watching the slow creep of the sun, from her dismal prison.

From where I crouched in the darkness, stones pressing into my spine, I could hear the drip, drip, drip of the water from the ceiling. Steam flowed across the floor, caught by the oculus of sunlight, moving like smoke, like breath. And now the hair on the back of my neck prickled as if the trapped spirit of an executed soul were curled in the dark beside me, waiting among the condemned, for a lover who had left her to die.

Chapter Two

Ocean

The Wanderer and the Hall

I have been wandering and no good has come of it. On my travels I have drifted at the ankles of the cliffs, my hands fettered by frost, fingertips split by the cold. I have spun very far from home, to where the ice breaks like knuckles of bone through the water. Unheard, my cries have mingled with the calls of the *ganot* and I have known myself forgotten. Just one hope remains, as the sleet melts on my skin: the faith that my suffering will pass, if only in the life to come.

Always I have been disappointed. My heart has raced to the promise of warmth and laughter, imagining days among brothers in the hall. It has fallen back to see that the halls were nothing but ruins hung about with icicles, the fine patterned stone charred by long extinguished fires and obscured by hoar frost. I have seen the work of giants standing empty in places that had once resounded with song; God was returning them to the realm of worm and woodlouse, binding them with root and stem.

I used to long for a warrior's life, with a generous lord and kinsmen for whom I would die. I imagined all the nights spent feasting in the hall, singing, rich in treasure, eager for war. We would be loyal to each other, strong in battle, and fight side by side. But I woke from these dreams alone on the freezing ocean and there I have remained.

Throughout my lonely exile, I have sung the old songs that once carried over the heath from the hall to my place at my mother's breast. I learned them there and now I have shaped them here with lips cracked by the sea. I mouthed into the gale the story of Theodric who tyrannised a city for thirty winters. I saw him hovering over the water, enthroned, grim-faced, blood on his metal hands. And I whispered the refrain:

'Their ordeal passed away, so too, in time, will mine!'

I remembered the torments borne by the famous Geat for Matilda, saw him rolling, sleepless, on the waves, pining for her affection.

'His ordeal passed away; so too, in time, will mine!'

Then I thought of Weland, hamstrung and enslaved, shaping teeth into jewels. I thought of his victim Beadohild, scared to tell her father she was pregnant. I thought of all the suffering endured in the long ages of this world.

'Their ordeals passed away,' I wept. 'So too, in time, will mine.'

The sea ice knocked at my boat. All earthly things, I understand, bliss as well as pain, will one day be no more. When the fire burns and everyone assembles, the fathomless ocean will roll on. As the men walk from their benches to receive golden rings from their lord, somewhere else the exile shivers and weeps. Even as they return to their seats and the embraces of their friends, there are sunless realms where the leviathan lies in wait. When they die, in battle or the sea, or in the heat of a fever, what good will their fame bring, or their beloved gold? What is the glint of the hall's light compared to the vast, dark belly of the ocean? It is better to accept my exile than long for joy that cannot be sustained.

So it was that this evening, when I saw the golden hall on the shoreline, its lights reaching out across the water. I wanted to pass it by, as the wise man would. And yet, try as I might, I was unable to turn away. In spite of everything, I picked up my cold paddle and struck out for the coast, towards the light of the hall. This was the familiar land in which I grew. I entered the mouth of the river and paddled against the currents until I had floated into a mist-banded marsh. I found a sturdy jetty, moored my boat and clambered up among the strands of sedge. As I approached the hall and traced its boundary I saw the serpents carved on the beams that face the gable, lit by a single, swinging lamp, and heard laughter coming from inside.

When I reached the doors, I paused. What could

go wrong? I imagined myself pushing them open. The great chamber is full of people, men, women and children lining the walls, and warriors assembling before the dais, on which the lord sits with his queen. They will be surprised to see me, but welcoming, surely?

My hand hovered before the latch as I imagined the lord's splendour, a circlet glowing on his dark hair and garnets on his shoulders. I pictured him beckoning me in with a hand just as bright with jewels, the warmth in his gesture even brighter. A young man will offer me his seat and I will sit. Food will be placed before me and I will eat, watching the lord distribute treasure, sharing blades and pommels set with stones, seeing the people laughing and singing. A child will keep trying to catch my eye and hiding when she succeeds, and the youth who gave up his seat will return time and again to pour mead into my horn. Though I stand beneath the dripping eaves, it was as if my feet could feel the warmth.

The cold of the sea clung to my shoulders as I let myself summon the later hours, when most of the company would have made beds beside the benches, their breathing rising and falling with the sound of the wind beyond the hall. I will sit myself at the edge of a group of warriors, the lord among them, gathered at the hearth. Their faces will be familiar to me now, as will mine to them: the face of a friend. Listening to their tales, I will wait till it is very late and the talking has faded, then will I break my silence.

'I have suffered so much,' I will tell them, 'I have learned that we pass through the bright days of our lives like birds through the beams. But tonight is different. Tonight your hospitality has made me happier than I have been in a very long time.'

I will stop there, even though I want to say more about the ruined walls, the uselessness of gold, the futility of glory, the vast, blank-faced ocean. I won't be able to. The words, faced with so much warmth, so much friendship, will refuse to rise to my mouth.

'Wassail,' *Be well*, the youth will say, and lift his cup, others following his lead. The lord will reach back to put his hand on my shoulder.

'Drinchail,' I will say, finding voice in custom, and bring the shining drink to my lips.

I imagined all of this and it seemed so real to me that my hand closed on the latch. When I was a child, living with my mother in her damp cave, she told me never to enter the hall, no matter how warm it seemed, no matter how welcoming.

'You are not like them,' she used to say, stroking my forehead as I lay in her arms. 'They will attack you and, when you fight back, they will blame you. Never go to the hall. Never open the door.'

But I could hear them laughing and talking and I didn't want to return to the ocean, to the ice and the unfeeling cry of the *ganot*, and I did not want to go home with nothing to tell my mother but tales of lonely wanderings. I told myself she was mistaken and that they did not call me Cain's kin, good only for showing, in death, the strength of their heroes. She was wrong to say they think me, think us, incapable of salvation. I wiped the water droplets from my face and lifted the latch. As the door creaked open, a slice of light showed me my own, monstrous arm. But still I stepped into the warmth of the hall, daring to believe that this would be the night on which the suffering of Grendel would also pass away.

I am racing over the heath and the blood is cooling on my skin. I don't know how many I killed, only that the terror overtook me and they were so angry, so wild with their swords and spears. I know I should return to my boat and exile on the ocean, but all I want is my mother and the safety of our cave.

In geographical terms, early medieval scholars held the ocean to constitute the waters that encircled the land. This makes sense if you look at surviving medieval maps, derived from Classical models, which often show Europe, Africa and Asia surrounded by the Ocean like a border.

An important characteristic of the ocean and its seas was the tides. In Isidore of Seville's *Etymologies*, the tides are characterised as 'a restlessness', and it was the ocean's restlessness, as well as its separation from the habitable parts of the world, that gave it rich metaphorical potential.

The Old English poem *The Seafarer* is narrated by one who has been compelled to wander the freezing ocean. Its main theme – earthly transience – is shared by another Exeter Book elegy, *The Wanderer*, whose narrator is a former warrior. They feature pathless expansive seas, lonely wanderings, and imaginative journeys from the waves to abandoned ruins that once rang with laughter. With vivid descriptions of wild, stormy seascapes, they argue for the ultimate transience of all earthly pleasure and pain, exhorting the reader to embrace the Christian message of eternal life.

The Seafarer and *The Wanderer* describe exile on the narrators' plight in ways that sometimes seem chillingly literal. These are poems born of an itinerant, seafaring society, made up of migrants and the descendants of migrants, for whom the perils of deep water and cruel weather were still sharp in the collective memory, if not present in everyday life. At the same time they present exile on the ocean as a metaphor for psychological turmoil. Take these heart-rending lines from the former:

> And so my spirit roams beyond the heart's restraints.
> My mind casts off on the swollen sea,
> eddies freely in the whale's wake,
> spins to the edges of the earth, then returns to me,
> restless and ravenous. Again, the lonely flier cries,
> prompting my powerless heart back to the way of the whale,
> onto the sweep of the sea.

The lonely soul scouring a wilderness whose paths are known only to the whale is contrasted with the soul of the warrior, surrounded by companions in the hall. The narrator recalls taking part in the traditional rituals of gift-giving that bound a Germanic lord to his thanes. He acknowledges the happiness of the memory, yet knows he can never relive it.

With lines famously echoed by Tolkien, the narrator of *The Wanderer* expresses the same melancholic nostalgia for bygone days:

> Where has the horse gone? Where has the man gone?
>   Where have the treasure-givers gone?
> Where are the seats at the feast? Where are the joys of
>   the hall?
> So long to the sparkling cup. So long to the warrior in
>   wargear.
> So long to princely power. See how that era has passed,
> faded into nothingness under night's helmet, as if it
>   had never been.

Here we can visualise a theatre of Germanic warrior culture: the extraordinary treasures that would have passed between battle-hardened hands by the light of flickering flames, the unity of the feast in the hall and the security of a benevolent lord. The poems evoke a golden age, an idea of heroes and lords composed when its real-life counterpart was already becoming a thing of the past. Despite the Christian philosophical note on which these poems conclude, they convey the perceived importance of community in the midst of a hostile natural and political world. Exclusion from that community might even be said to have been a fate worse than death. Indeed, the Old

English elements of our modern word 'forlorn' translate as 'utterly lost'.

I met the Seafarer in person in January 2020, in a spontaneous lock-in at a local pub. The evening had begun as a wassail, a traditional New Year event in rural England, and a troop of morris-dancing folk singers had struck up in the snug. The night was as raucous as they come and culminated in the barmaid dancing on the table. She was a woman in middle years sporting a medieval-wench costume and abundant tattoos depicting the faces of her pets. It was one of those brilliant evenings in which complete strangers come together by chance, make lots of noise and eventually melt back into the night feeling as though the world is a loving place, after all. At one in the morning, just before everyone was readying to leave, a man who had spent the whole time sitting at the bar ruffling the ears of his handsome lurcher, told us he was an ex-serviceman who had experienced periods of depression and that for the past few hours he had felt happier than he had in a long time. We toasted his health and the health of his dog. It gave the wassail, which means 'be well' in Old English, even greater poignancy.

The only issue with spinning a story from poems like *The Seafarer* and *The Wanderer* (and also another Exeter Book elegy called *Deor* that would take us too far from the ocean to discuss here) is the Everyman quality of their narrators. However, I know of at least one exiled figure from Old English literature who does receive careful characterisation. He is the first antagonist in *Beowulf* and a fitting inaugural kill for its eponymous hero.

The epic tale tells us how Beowulf, still a young warrior, is called to deliver the hall, Heorot, from nightly terrorisation by a monster. This monster is a descendant of Cain – the first murderer, according to the Old Testament – and his name is Grendel. The *Beowulf* narrator dwells on Grendel's motivations, explaining how the sounds of singing, the harp, of joy and revelry in the hall, tormented him in his home in the wilderness. I am not the first writer to sympathise with this anti-hero and I won't be the last, but here I have imagined Grendel as *The Seafarer*. I have imagined him hoping to enjoy the kind of respite found by the ex-serviceman at the wassail night. Of course, in the *Beowulf* narrative, Grendel has no such luck. His encounter with the hall awakens within him a terrible desire for revenge that sees him fleeing back to the underwater home of his monstrous mother.

For all the hostility of the inhabitants of Heorot towards Grendel, real Germanic societies may not have been so cruel. Tacitus, a Roman historian who died in the second century CE, writes how:

> no nation indulges more freely in feasting and entertaining than the German. It is accounted a sin to turn any man away from your door. The host welcomes his guest with the best meal that his means allow. When he has finished entertaining him, the host undertakes a fresh role: he accompanies the guest to the nearest house where further hospitality can be had. It makes

no difference that they come uninvited; they are welcomed just as warmly. No distinction is ever made between acquaintance and stranger as far as the right to hospitality is concerned.

This picture is corroborated by the Norse myths, collated by Snorri Sturluson in the thirteenth century, in which Odin's regular visits to strange halls depend on his expectation of customary hospitality.

In March 2020, only two months after the wassail lock-in, Britain went into lockdown. By the end of the year the pub had boarded its windows and I still wonder how the man with the dog fared through it all. He demonstrated to me the timelessness of the tale of exile told by the Old English elegies. Now that the worst of the pandemic seems to be over, their guarantee that all things pass resonates as well. The ocean-wild presents itself in these poems as a powerful metaphor for the experience of psychological suffering: the feeling of being restless and alone. But there is hope in the restlessness; hope in perpetual change.

Chapter Three

Forest

The Wildman, the Waterfall
and the Wind

Lying on my belly, I creep to the edge and hang my head over the side of the gorge. Mist clings to my beard and cheeks, and in the distance the waterfall roars. My heart dances in my chest and I close my eyes to the sensation of the wind stirring the hair on my back. I am always naked now and have come to enjoy the sensations it brings. Once, when I was tall and muscular, a tunic stretched tight across me. But as time passed, I got more sick and my clothing began to hang in loose swathes and fill with holes until it fell away altogether and I did not bother to pick it up.

The sound of the waterfall is a relief. It drowns

out the cries of the birds that have been my constant companions since I was driven into the forest. They are maddening to me. They would madden you too if their shadows circled wherever you went, and their voices, starting at dawn, feel like scattered taunts upon you for your exile, illness and ugliness: cuckoo, falcon, blackbird, with their carbuncle eyes, with their blade-bright beaks. Always their songs patter on my head and back like a blizzard of snail shells, but here the waterfall drowns them out. The wind and the water cause the treetops to clap their budded twigs, while, far below, the rocks gnash their teeth.

The wind strengthens and I grip my staff with fingers gnawed by disease and insect bites and raise myself to standing, knees and feet scraping the rocks, the shiver of stone travelling up my limbs. I am sick. I want to be as alive as I was when I let the seasons hurry by in all their varied hues, when I had the strength to wield an axe, cleave a trunk and build a house. I want to touch my daughter's hair and play with her by the firelight. I want to kiss my wife. I have whiled and wasted away in the forest and become something apart from people, a kind of beast.

Through the trees and the chasm, the wind and water cascade. I remember how I looked when I last saw my reflection in the lake, before the mist invaded my eyes and birdsong cracked the shell of my mind. Even then, a veil of matted hair had begun to cover my skin, and my nose was wasting away. So long ago. How must I look now? Like the burdock seed, all clawed and hairy. I let go of my staff and it drops into the ravine. The wind rises.

There has been one comfort since my exile: my dear Sweeney. I picture him as I knew him when he first arrived: a distant, naked form in the treetop. From the heights he spoke his sympathy for a fellow outcast, in his strange, quiet voice he vowed he would protect me. I promised the same in return. He from the canopy, me from the understorey, we shared the dramas of our madness. For drowning a Psalter in a lake, a saint placed a curse of perpetual flight upon him; my lord cursed me as punishment for an ill-considered jest. My illness grew like a fungus, choking, eclipsing the light, until my mind and body were filled with toadstools. As night fell, I said to my dear friend Sweeney:

'Will you tell me if a raven croaks where the trees are darkest?'

'I will.'

'You will not let the screech-owl fly over me in the night?'

'Never, Ealladhan.'

I asked Suibhne to sleep two trees distant, but even from there he was able to drive away the birds. In his presence, by the sound of his lilting songs, the branches seemed less tangled, the trees less dark with spite, my mind less soft with rot.

He stayed with me for a year and as the seasons passed, I showed him what to eat. We savoured the best crops of hawthorn buds, cherry fruits, wood sorrel and sweet dandelion leaves. We gathered the small stony-seeded fruits of the wild service tree. I plucked strawberries from trailing stems and he twisted small green apples from the highest boughs. As the leaves bleached and fell, fragrant mushrooms rose. We feasted on the bounty of the forest and cared for each other, but I feared it couldn't last. He left the forest a month ago when I told him I had an appointment to keep with a waterfall and the wind.

Two-stepping through the din, the call of a cuckoo chases the last strength from my limbs. I hear its claws scratching the bark. I hear its feathers shifting. In the canopy, the twigs bow towards me.

Just in time, I lift my arms and the wind rushes down, gathering strength. Then, like the palm of a giant, open hand, it slams into my back and pushes me forward. I do not resist. I have become so frail that I don't know if I could have fought it anyway. I slide off the cliff like a leaf, cast over the edge and spinning, falling, tumbling. The grey of rocks, the blue of the sky, the clapping hands of the trees, they roll past me. It is here, this moment for which I have longed. Now there will be no more birds, no more noise and pain, no more – I think of Sweeney wandering through the upper air and pray we will meet again. Let me die as the prophet foretold, by the hand of the wind, in the sudden black silence of the river.

Welsh and Irish nature poems dating from the eighth to the tenth century have a special predilection for the forest. In these verses it is the dwelling place, sometimes idyllic, sometimes hostile, of hermits and wildmen, as well as a vast array of creatures and birds. Two poems that are especially important here are the Irish *Buile Suibhne* and the Welsh *Claf Abercuawg*.

Buile Suibhne concerns a man called Suibhne (pronounced *Sweeney*) who has been cursed to fly, wandering wild places, until death by a spear. For some of his exile, he travels from Ireland to Ailsa Craig, a volcanic outcrop off the coast of Scotland's South Ayrshire. From there he makes his way to mainland Britain and, alighting in a forest, meets a renowned wildman, or 'Fer Caille', called Ealladhan.

By now, exile in the wilderness has driven both men to insanity and they live together for a year, separated by the space of two trees, guarding each other from imagined dangers in the cries of birds. The relationship, with its frisson of romance, has recently been explored by poet Seán Hewitt. But it is doomed. When the year is up, the wildman, Ealladhan, takes himself off to a waterfall, where it has been prophesied that the wind will push him to his death and his soul will journey to heaven.

The *Claf Abercuawg* portrays the plight of one exiled to the forest due to leprosy. The narrator describes symptoms of the illness, especially weight loss and depression, alongside the forbidding, oppressive forest: ivy, oak and the relentless calling of the cuckoo:

> I have listened to a cuckoo on an ivy-covered tree.
> My clothing has become loose.
> Grief for that which I loved is greater.
> [. . .]
> Noisy are the birds; wet the shingle
> Leaves fall; the exile is dispirited.
> I will not deny I am ill tonight.

As both the Fer Caille in *Buile Suibhne* and the narrator of *Claf Abercuawg* are exiled in a British forest, I have taken the liberty of merging them into one character. Doing so gives the anonymous leprosy sufferer a name, a friendship and a death. However, for all his individual attributes, he is an iteration of one stock character: the wildman.

The forest-dwelling wildman has deep roots. Sometimes, especially in later medieval depictions, he is young and muscular to the point of rapacious monstrosity, but early sources often present him as old, frail and associated with strange prophetic wisdom and madness. He goes by many names: Wildman, wodewose, Lailoken, Myrddin Wyllt, Merlin Silvestris, Fer Caille.

One ancient glimpse of this figure that certainly influenced the character of the medieval wildman is the portrayal of Nebuchadnezzar in Judaeo-Christian Scripture. The Book of Daniel, in many ways folkloric, eddies with prophetic dreams, divine portents and eschatological themes, that is, stories of end times. Among its most prominent subjects is the wealthy and powerful King Nebuchadnezzar, who suffers exile for seven years in the wilderness: 'He was driven away from among men, and did eat grass like an ox, and his body was wet with the dew of heaven: till his hairs grew like the feathers of eagles, and his nails like birds' claws' (Daniel 4: 33).

An Old English version of the Book of Daniel exists in a manuscript known as 'Junius 11', dated to around the year 1000. It also tells the story of Nebuchadnezzar, explaining that the King, formerly proud and arrogant, was reduced in the wild to the state of a beast, without human intelligence. It describes how he wandered the paths of the deer, until, after seven years, he returned to his throne 'humbler in his thinking', and 'recounted to his people his wanderings, the widely nomadic trail he had roamed in the company of wild beasts'. His sojourn in the wild brings him wisdom.

Another important Scriptural example of the wildman may be found in the biblical figure of John the Baptist who prophesies the arrival of Christ. He is said to have worn camel hair and lived on locusts and wild honey. In medieval art, he is shown with long, shaggy hair, a tunic made of rough animal hide, and bare feet. Likewise, in representations of the first Christian saints, those who flee to a lonely life in the landscape are often shown covered from head to toe in hair. Among them is the reformed courtesan Mary of Egypt, depicted with long tresses covering her nakedness like a cloak.

Monks under the auspices of the Irish Church valued the example of John the Baptist and those early saints, influencing the culture of the monasteries its missionaries founded in Northumbria from the early seventh century, converting the Germanic pagans who had settled the south-east coast of Britain. This monastic culture had a particular love of asceticism, which, in its extreme, took the form of the strict self-denial of the lonely hermit. It saw Irish and

Northumbrian monks taking themselves off to remote islands to live in prayer and seclusion. In Ireland, this impulse gave rise to a literary genre known as hermit poetry. Describing the perfect woodland hermitage, *The Song of Manchín of Líath* reads:

> A beautiful wood close by
> Around it on every side
> For the nurture of many-voiced birds
> To shelter and hide it.
>
> Facing the south for warmth,
> A little stream across its ground,
> A choice plot with abundant bounties
> Which would be good for every plant.

In the solitude of a hermitage, or the disciplined communal life of the cloister, men and women could contemplate Scripture and exercise restraint, bringing into balance their volatile humanity. From these secluded communities and hermits came exquisitely worked metal, swirling with the trumpet spirals typical of Celtic metalwork as old as the Iron Age. Their designs translated from gold and silver to the pages of manuscripts that vibrate with interlace and coils, colour and creatures. But for all its idealisation, the more extreme eremitic lifestyles were hard, and not without risk of achieving the opposite goal. The wild could be a dangerous place as much due to over-abundance as due to privation.

In the seclusion of the wild, the mind could fall foul of its unruly ways; the hermit or the exile could become the wildman. In the Welsh and Latin literature of the twelfth century, the figure of Merlin crystallises as one who has fled to the woods after a battle in which he saw the heavens open above him. His sister worries and takes him food to see him through the winter. He is able to tame the creatures of the forest and is party to secret knowledge, such as the Queen's illicit love affair. He is portrayed as the child of an incubus demon (of the kind trapped in Guthlac's barrow) and a nun from Carmarthen. Like Fer Caille in *Buile Suibhne*, he predicts the manner of his own death.

The character of Merlin may preserve a much older notion of the moral complexity of the wildman.

Much is lost regarding pre-Christian Celtic beliefs, but surviving depictions of the Roman deity Silvanus, god of woods and wild lands, show a naked old man with thick curly hair and beard, a crown of pine and cloak of animal skins.

The wildman endured in the popular imagination well into the Middle Ages. Nowhere was he more memorably celebrated, nor more shockingly punished, than at a party in the fourteenth-century court of King Charles VI of France. It was 28 January 1393, and six revellers, including the King himself, performed a dance in the guise of wildmen. Charles VI had been exhibiting symptoms of mental ill-health and per-haps the event was intended to bring him some relief. However, their costumes were made of fibres stuck in place with an inflammable resin. Cavorting too close to a flame, one of the dancers caught fire. Before long, the fire had leapt to the other dancers, burning four of them to death. The Duchess of Berry is said to have saved the King's life by covering his burning body with her skirts. Even in the carefully choreographed realm of the later medieval court, the wildman brought the elemental chaos of the forest.

As with Merlin, the wildman's natural home is alone in the deepest, darkest forest: an all-consuming place, a dark place. In Plato's *Timaeus* (written in the fourth century BCE), the Demiurge, the first artisan or maker, forges the universe out of unformed matter. The Ancient Greek word for this 'matter' was translated by fourth-century-CE writer Calcidius as *silva*, meaning 'forest' in Latin. To Calcidius, whose work circulated in the courts, cloisters and cathedral schools of medieval Europe, chaos and forests were synonymous.

I saw Calcidius' *silva* as I wandered through the kaleidoscopic landscape of Selwood Forest in Somerset. It is a fragment of the old medieval hunting forest of Wessex: a formidable natural barrier that I visit often and only ever leave by luck. That is to say, I enter Selwood and get lost as a matter of principle. Here, only the yellow hazel catkins dangling like pendants made straight lines. Here, the ground beneath my feet was a ragbag of last year's leaves, entering a grave of acorns, sharp chestnut husks and broken twigs, pierced by blades of grass. Look higher than the ground and, on one side, a holly grove, hostile and fat, on another, pendulous sedge, waving its tapering leaves beneath a bough crested with orange fungi. Above all these, an ink splatter of birches and oaks, elbowing their way to the light, here a sinuous bulge to buttress against the wind, there a high branch wedged in the armpit of a neighbour.

I wonder how I would have felt if, among the fallen leaves, I had seen the imprint of a bare human foot. Then, hearing a twig snap behind me, what if I had turned to see a man, emaciated and hairy, picking his way between the trunks like a wandering deer? What if he avoided my gaze and spoke to himself in low tones, lifting his eyes at the call of a blackbird and moving past me until the shadows of the holly grove covered his whiskered back? More fool me for stepping into his home. The wisdom of the wildman is couched in madness. He is the excess of the forest.

Chapter Four

Beast

The Mountain on my Back

'I have a present for you, Etheldreda,' he said, passing me a bundle of silks.

'Thank you.'

I took it from him and ran my hands over the material, making out the straight edges and hard corners of the object underneath. His eyes were on my face as I unwrapped the covering of whatever bribe he had hidden inside. A small casket made of – of what? – a pale material, like ivory. Its metal fittings glowed in the low light from the window. I held it up.

Carved scenes decorated the surface of the casket and I recognised one straightaway. It showed the image of the Virgin and Child receiving gifts from the Magi. I smiled, disarmed by the intricacy of the craftsmanship and the gentle articulation of the figures, a beauty that caused the chamber, the view of the ocean and distant monastery, even his eager face, to recede.

I rotated the casket in my hands and found Romulus and Remus suckling the She-Wolf. I saw the tale of Hos and my heartbeat quickened at the thought of her plight. But there were more scenes – the violation of the Temple in Jerusalem? I wanted to stand up and take the casket to the window, see it more clearly in the light from the sunset, but his voice cut through my concentration.

'You like it, then?'

'I . . . Yes, it is beautiful.'

'It was carved by one of the nuns at Streoneshalh.'

I drew my eyes away to look at him: the boy, only fifteen years old, some ten years younger than me and, as of two days ago, my husband. I knew why he had gone to this expense; I knew he wanted me to come to his room tonight, as I had failed to do since our wedding. Surely he realised I did not intend to. Not tonight, not ever. That was clear to me now.

On impulse, I sat down and put my hand on his, at once disturbed to see him comforted by the motherly gesture.

'I am grateful for your care,' I said, 'but I am tired and would like to go to sleep.'

Then, hoping I misread the flash of malice in his eyes, I added, truthfully, 'It is a wonderful present.'

He looked as if he were about to say something, but his beardless chin shook and the words did not come. Was he angry, or humiliated? He half rose and leaned forward to kiss me, but with an intake of breath I turned my face away, so that his lips brushed against my cheek. I did not look at him as he left. Someone else, someone framed differently from me, would have his child and I would say nothing, I would happily let her provide the heir to inherit his sea-battered kingdom. I had thought I had no choice but to marry him, but now I knew I could never let him touch me as he wanted to. Now as in my former life, it was not in my power to allow it.

Once the door had closed behind him, I went

to the window and held the casket up to the light. I saw a man holding a pair of tongs over an anvil in one hand and a cup in another. He was passing it to a woman: I recognised it as Weland, giving a drugged drink to Beadohild. Her face was turned towards mine, as if beseeching me to alter her fate. She would be intoxicated, raped and impregnated. What a strange companion to the Virgin Mary, whose image was beside her, who granted her womb willingly to God for the incarnation of His Son.

Not without a stab of envy did I send thoughts of praise along the coast to the nun who carved these scenes. The convent and monastery at Streoneshalh were barely three years old and I imagined the community walking the pristine corridors, reading together, tending the gardens and working in the workshops for crafting Scripture, metal and ivory.

The sun had nearly set and I considered lighting a lamp so that I could keep looking at the casket, perhaps attempt to decipher the runes encircling Beadohild and the Virgin, but I put it down, too tired.

Something was tugging at the hem of my mind, wanting my attention. I should lie down and shut my eyes.

The servants knew not to come to me as I got ready for bed. I put on my nightgown and slid between the cool sheets, relishing the scent of lavender on my pillow, the sweet musk of the linen and my solitude. Safe from all the demands of the day, I rested my head, but as I tried to find what it was that was asking for my attention, a solution to a problem that was eager to make itself known, I fell asleep. From there, I entered into a dream.

I am lying on a beach. My mind is awash with anger at my neglect: how they let the water dry from my eyes and lips, and let my weight settle on the sand. They let me starve, let brine crust on my tongue till the sight of their fearful faces throbbed with each beat of my perishing heart. When my life had left me, I clung as spirit to my bones. I watched as they came with lances and burst me open. In their hordes, they stripped away the skin and fat and buried my entrails in a pit. When just the white forest of my skeleton remained, foliated at first with flesh, nourishment for the birds, then bleached bright by the sun and bitter sleet, they put their hands on me. *Let me crumble to sand dunes,* I willed the ground, *to slide back to the sea in which I grew to my full strength.* But the men did not let me be.

Saws cut through my jaw and they took me in sections over the cliffs. They laid me in the hands of a nun, who took me to her workshop and secured me in the mouth of a vice. As her brow furrowed and her breath shook the small hairs on her lip, I gnashed my teeth. *I am here,* I said. *Can't you hear me?*

Her lack of fear angered me. Did she not know who I was? When I was alive they called me a monster. Then I could see the men's boat from beneath – a dark oval on my blue-domed domain – and set my course ahead of theirs: faster, faster, till I was a day out of sight. Then I pushed my back above the waves, my great rocky back, with its semblance of mountains and lush valleys, wooded countries and calm, fish-filled lakes. As the water poured off me, I shut my eyes and waited, still as the earth itself. And they, drawing closer in their boat, saw me and thought me a safe place to make land and seek shelter. They wandered across my skin and kindled a fire. But the touch of heat against me told me my scheme had worked. As I breathed my great breath, they realised their mistake and tried to run to their boats, scrabbled for their ropes and jumped into the waters. But I, with my lungs full, plunged down before one soul could evade me, gathering them in my undertow, pulling them into the abyss. In the darkness of the deep, deep ocean, I dragged them to their deaths.

Holding me in the vice, working at me with metal tools, the nun did not represent my mischief. She wasn't even scared. She carved scenes, she drilled and riveted, she fitted a delicate lock. Wrenched from my element, I languished. Caught beneath the bright gaze of kings and princes, I am homesick for the abyss.

I woke from the dream and stared into the darkness. For a moment I believed I was at the bottom of the ocean, but then I heard, beyond my window, the waves breaking on the beach. It took a long moment for my heartbeat to slow and the sensation that my throat was full of salt to pass. Then a question took hold in my mind. I got out of my bed, lit a candle and picked up the casket. Finding Beadohild and the Virgin, my eye travelled to the runes that surrounded them. I tried voicing the letters aloud, and though I did not manage it the first time, nor the second, eventually I discerned and spoke words:

'The king of terror became sad when he swam on to the shingle. Whale's bone.'

Not ivory, then. I thought of the great whale of which I had read as a child, the one called Iasconius, its body withered to bone, its bone dragged, perhaps, from the very beaches my window overlooked. Iasconius was famed for its deceitful ways, pretending to be a safe island, luring sailors to its back, then dragging them to their deaths. And all at once I had to grasp the bed, the room shifting under my feet as if I were about to slide into deep water. I shut my eyes until stillness returned. When I opened them again, the casket shone white and flawless in the dark. So too did the new knowledge that had troubled me as I had fallen asleep: that I too had been taken in. No more. The boy could beg, he could threaten, he could pursue me over the fens and kill me, but with the casket he had given me a greater gift than he knew: a message from its holy maker at Streoneshalh. I would go to her tomorrow.

I was standing on a beach in Whitby in the shadow of the weathered, plundered and bombarded Abbey ruins. From a modern viewpoint, north was ahead of me, towards the town and the flank of the east coast, up into the North Sea. That, after all, is the top of the compass. East was to my right, across the sea towards Northern Germany and Denmark. In the medieval imagination, however, East was the top of the map. Turning to face it, I looked out to sea, imagining myself on the westernmost edge of the world, with the sanctifying promise of Jerusalem, Eden and the sunrise before me. It is a constant source of wonder, viewing a familiar landscape through the lens of earlier ages.

Animals and birds likewise take on a whole new significance when viewed from a medieval perspective. In today's Whitby, a whale's mighty jawbones stand at the top of a flight of steps overlooking the town. The monument acknowledges the role of the whaling industry in the town's modern history, as well as the North Sea in establishing its wealth. However, had this monument stood in the same place thirteen hundred years ago, it would have held quite different connotations.

The Franks Casket (which we met in Chapter One) is an eighth-century whale's bone box that may have originated in Northumbria. As well as numerous scenes from Germanic, Christian and Classical legend, it bears a runic inscription on the front panel: 'The king of terror became sad when he swam on to the shingle. Whale's bone'. The text suggests that the bone was foraged from a carcass of a beached whale. Perhaps it came from one of the beaches near the centres of monasticism (and artistic production) that looked out to the North Sea – Lindisfarne, Hartlepool and Whitby among them – where a whale-bone vessel would have put viewers in mind of the Old Testament story of Jonah's three-day sojourn in the belly of the whale. The story of Jonah served, for Christian readers, as a prefiguration of the three days that passed before Christ's Resurrection (an approach to revealing how the New Testament fulfils the Old Testament known as 'typology'). During those three days, Christ is said to have undertaken the 'Harrowing of Hell', in which he redeemed all the good souls who had died before and offer imaginative moral lessons based on the three animals' curious behaviours. The iridescent panther lives in an earthly paradise, sleeps for three days, and awakes emitting from its mouth a music and fragrance so sweet that none can help but flock towards it. In this way it is an allegory for Christ's death and resurrection. The partridge steals the nests of other birds and incubates their eggs, but the chicks, discerning that their true parents are elsewhere, leave to find them. In this way, humans, raised under the belly of the devil, must seek out God, their true father. As for the whale, it pretends to be a pleasant island, tempting sailors to moor their boats to its shores, with the purpose of dragging them to their deaths. The whale represents the Devil, Lucifer, the Beast, who lures humanity into sin with temptations that seem pleasant and safe. 'Then all of a sudden, he surges in style, our sea-spectre taking them down on the salt-way. Bottom bound.'

The whale, or island-simulating sea-monster, has many wonderful names. In The Physiologus it is called

'Aspidochelone' or 'shield turtle'. The name 'Fastito-calon' is given in the Old English *Physiologus*-inspired poems of the Exeter Book. It appears too as 'Iasco-nius' in *The Voyage of St Brendan the Abbot*, an Irish epic (*íasc* is Old Irish for 'fish'), a hugely popular medieval text which survives in manuscripts from as early as the tenth century, in which a troop of Irish monks sailing the Atlantic disembark and build a fire on the whale but manage to hurry back to their boat before the creature dives. Only their holy leader, St Brendan, recognises the true nature of the island and remains in the boat. These names give it an ominous grandeur, befitting its colossal size and terrible malevolence.

When, as a student, I first encountered the Franks Casket, I wanted it to have been made by a woman, for a woman. My reasons were as follows. The front of the casket shows the legendary goldsmith Weland offering a drink to Beadohild, who we met in Chapter Two. She has come to the smithy in which he is imprisoned, not realising that he hates her and has already murdered her brothers. The drink is laced with soporific herbs and she is powerless to fight against him as he rapes her. In the artist's rendering of the scene, only the figure of Beadohild is shown facing the viewer. Her wide-eyed, oval face looks out, unaware that her brothers' corpses lie under the floor of the forge. If you know the story, you want to say to her, 'Please, Beadohild, don't drink, don't trust him!' The rape leads to her impregnation with the Germanic hero Widia.

The only other story illustrated on the front panel of the casket, beside Beadohild, shows the New Testament scene of the Three Wise Men offering gifts to the Virgin and Child. The Virgin, like Beadohild, looks directly out at the viewer, except, unlike Beadohild, she has consented to bear the child in her arms. What is more, the cup offered to her by the nearest Wise Man is a symbol of kingship rather than violence. It is not inconceivable that an eighth-century, educated Northumbrian woman would have seen the two female characters' respective fates as an expression of the dangers of secular life versus the independence and security of a Christian, perhaps even monastic, vocation.

There are other ways in which the casket plays with ideas of womanhood. Both Beadohild and the Virgin are vessels. The casket itself is a vessel. Moreover, thanks to the Old Testament story of Jonah, the animal from which the casket is made is a vessel. I don't think it's an exaggeration to say that the imagery on the casket, as well as its material, invites sympathy with the plight of women and the female body. Not only that, but it anticipates a learned viewer. Could it have been made at a double house (a monastery with women, as well as men) like the one at Streoneshalh in modern-day Whitby? If it had entered the possession of a well-educated secular woman, of which there was a burgeoning number, what meanings might she have teased from its material, images and text? Certainly many of the great religious women of early medieval Britain had lived secular lives before entering the cloister, such as Abbess Hild of Whitby and Abbess Etheldreda of Ely, who founded their respective institutions. The latter, born around 636, had two husbands, but is said to have remained committed to chastity. Her second husband, Ecgfrith of Northumbria, may have been as young as fourteen when they married. He refused to respect her wishes, nor her decision to enter a convent shortly after his accession to the throne, and legend preserves the tale of how he chased her across the fens to the Isle of Ely where she would found her Abbey. The whale's bone Franks Casket shows how animal lore could mix and meld with Scripture, as well as pre-Christian Germanic and Classical myth, giving rise to countless impressions and ideas. Study the Franks Casket and whole vistas of meaning seem to open up before your eyes.

Today, Whitby attracts those with a penchant for Bram Stoker's *Dracula* and a dark love of jewellery set with beads of Whitby jet (a fossilised ancestor of the monkey puzzle tree). However, in 664, Bishops flocked to the headland for the event now known as the Synod of Whitby. There, Abbess Hild presided over one of the most important political meetings

Chapter Five

Fen

Treasure Guardian

My brooch is a labyrinth of golden beasts whose mouths swallow their tails and whose eyes are beads of fire. My daughter used to believe it was the work of Weland. She believed the serpents would amaze the devil and hold him fast, but now she knows it is not so, for it is the fens that are the riddle, a maze of waterways, knotted with eels, in which the lost may never be found.

You'd be wrong to think that because we live in the wild we are artless. We are weavers, fishermen and smiths, and skilled in our trades. But there is savagery there, for our men were raised in a blood-feud with the islands beyond our own and they train as if battle were at dawn. They are vain, with their hairless bodies, their braided heads and their limbs like polished oak. They are like dogs eager for the hunt. And their minds are stretched across the silent mist, awaiting provocation. Few would have the guile to escape them.

While they feast at their lord's throne, my daughter walks the aisles and fills their cups. She shines by the torchlight. She decorates him, Eadwacer, whose name means 'treasure guardian', who presides from the dais with bright skin and a cruel smile. She is his finest jewel and he hopes one day to take his heir from her mineral womb. From my bench at the edge of the hall my stomach writhes; I hate him.

But I know that my daughter is not the slave he thinks her. I know that on those nights when he is drunk and grunting in his sleep, she slips from their bed, out into the windy night. She takes a shallow vessel from the jetty and slides into the waterway between the reed beds. The grasses whisper in urgent tongues, tossing their heads. She glides between them until she reaches the goat-headed tip of a sunken bough, then she turns to the darkest part of the horizon, away from the distant band of trees that marks the edge of the fen. The night-owl calls and the water gulps each stroke of the pole, and then she comes to an altar formed of the upended bole of a tree, its lower half stained dark by the mud of winter tides. It lies halfway between our island and the island where she would tread, as her lover would on ours, on pain of death. He waits for her there, plaiting reeds with his back resting on the blackened roots. Then my daughter calls:

'Wulf. My Wulf.'

He turns. Perhaps, like us, he comes from the older people of the fens, the ones whose bodies we find curled in the peat. His hair is dark, his limbs lean and agile.

Their meetings on the altar are sacred. And now that she has conceived a child, my daughter longs to escape.

'Wulf, my Wulf, my longing for you has made me sick, not just for lack of food.'

On darker nights, when the raindrops worry the thatch, Eadwacer wraps his limbs around her. She despises the smooth weight of his body and thinks of how she might return to Wulf. On these nights she cries, and by day she can hardly eat or discern whether the pain she feels is caused by the infant within her or the life for which she yearns. She pictures Wulf wandering alone on the gold-green blade of the horizon and turns her face towards it. I read it on her brow, how she aches from all the wishing, how she cannot wait a moment longer than she has to. Her pain is visible and I beg her to let me help.

When the time comes for her to deliver, I stand beside her for two whole days. I wonder if I could bear to lose her for the sake of a child I do not yet know, but then something shifts within her and she survives. She bears a son and we take it in turns to hold him, wondering at his beauty.

The very next night, I paddle the shallow vessel to the goat-headed bough, pushing through the reeds with trembling arms for I have hardly eaten or slept. I turn to the darkest part of the sky and approach the altar. There I leave my brooch, its patterned surface reflecting the tangled fens. Wulf knows what to do. When he finds this treasure he will wait for night to descend, and then he will follow the plan.

This afternoon I am certain the sun takes longer to set than it should. I sit at my daughter's bedside, cradling my grandson, offering her feverfew for the pain. Our bag is under the bed. I nudge it with my foot, to reassure myself it is there. Then at last the bedsheets brighten with the sunset. Let Eadwacer stay late in the hall tonight, let him drink himself to the grave.

And then night has fallen and I have gathered my grandson to my chest and stolen to the jetty. I have hidden with him in a boat among the reeds, where we will wait for Wulf's signal. My daughter emerges, just visible in the light from the hall window. She is slow, raw, breathing hard and watching the path, anxious not to fall. When her hand touches the post of the jetty, she stops.

'Is he sleeping?' she says, her voice no louder than the reeds.

'Yes,' I say.

And then we hear the ripple of oars. The one she calls Wulf is here, rowing past our island, just as we planned, but he must make it further downstream, towards the coast and the forested headland, before Eadwacer realises they are here. I hold my breath and rest my lips on my grandson's soft new cheek.

Someone douses the fire in the hall and the light from its windows goes out. Now only moonlight remains. A shout comes from inside Eadwacer's chamber. He has noticed that my daughter and the baby are gone. I hear the sound of running feet and will Wulf to row faster.

I dare to look through the reeds towards the river, snaking away towards the distant bank of trees, mud and water glistening by the light of the moon. I release my breath. Wulf has made good progress and now he is far enough past the hall for it to take time for Eadwacer to reach them. I can see Wulf has stood up on the boards of the vessel, a silhouette but for the white shape of a baby's swaddling cloth bundled in his arms.

And now Eadwacer is outside, calling my daughter's name. Knowing what she must do, she reaches out her arm and points across the reed beds to Wulf. Her voice rings like a hammer:

'Can you hear me, Eadwacer? Wulf is taking our poor whelp to the woods!'

And Eadwacer, running to the jetty, sees Wulf floating towards the trees, the bundle in his arms. And the old warrior's features shatter, the ancient feud that has for so long bound our islands giving roots to this insult, this unforgivable crime. And now his men are joining him, ready to attack. Looking forward to a kill. He gets into one of the larger boats and his men follow, untying the rope, pushing off into the flow, the ring-patterned steel of their swords reflecting the moonlight. They leave my daughter standing on the jetty and they pass my hiding place by. They are following the way to the forest, after Wulf and the child they imagine he carries in his arms.

The marsh has swallowed the noises of the men, so that I can hear only our breathing and the chirp,

chirp, chirp of the summer's last crickets. We are safe but we must act quickly. My daughter crawls off the jetty and steps through the reeds. She slides, muddy-limbed, into the boat, lowering herself onto the blankets I laid there for her. She kisses the sleeping infant as I pass him into her arms, then we lean together, the briefest acknowledgement of love. But her jaw is set and I know what she is thinking. Wulf said that he knew secret ways where Eadwacer could not find him, that he would survive to come and find us in the fens. I cannot allay her fear, nor can I worry about what Wulf will do yet. For now I must protect my children with all the cunning I have. I pick up the paddle and push the vessel into the river. Then I make for one of the smaller streams between the ranks of whispering reeds. May the riddling fens confuse the devil. May we never be found.

In Old English, *fenne* is a generic term for wetland, fen, marsh or bog. Fens, in our sense of the word, are areas of wetland characterised by peaty soil and expansive beds of sedges, rushes and reeds. The Fens, proper, are found in the low-lying coastal region of eastern England. Place-names, among many other kinds of evidence, show that tribes who would come to call themselves the English settled the 'islands' of the Fens and neighbouring wetlands from the start of the migration of Germanic tribes around the fourth century CE. These tribes had roots in territories of western Germany and southern Scandinavia that were just as rich in clammy soils, perilous bogs and vast, flat, uncultivated terrains, and people's imaginative connection to them had deep, winding roots.

Fenland provides the setting for the Exeter Book Old English elegy *Wulf and Eadwacer*. Its nineteen alliterative lines (rhyme is rare in Old English poetry) are narrated by a woman, who tells us of her separation from one called 'Wulf' by wetlands and the hostility of her people. She describes how the mysterious Wulf wanders far and wide as she weeps in the rain, 'dogged' by hopes. The bestial limbs of a warrior embrace her of the poem, Wulf could be the enemy, but I didn't want to do that here. For me, Eadwacer was the same warrior who had constrained her with animal limbs, while Wulf was someone free and wild for whom she yearned. Perhaps descended from the earliest Germanic Gyrwas who inhabited the Fens (a later medieval source says 'gyr' means 'deep bog'), having settled the East Coast with the first migrating tribes, or else from the Britons, whose people had dominated the region since before the Roman occupation. Searching for answers sends us down meandering waterways that bring us back to where we started, I hope because there is no answer to be found. But the feeling that the poem is a mere glimpse of something more substantial is one of the secrets to its power.

The morning on which I visited the landscape evoked in *Wulf and Eadwacer* felt like the pivot point between winter and spring. I was tightrope-walking the dry ridge through the reed beds on the eastern edge of England, thinking about riddles, interlace and marshes, and breathing the sedge-sweet air, which bore traces of the sea. Golden stems and fluffy seed-heads hushed and jostled in their millions on my right and, on my left, they flanked a low river. It shone like mercury, sliding between the dimpled and buxom mudbanks. I was at Snape, not far from Sutton Hoo, the site of one of the most important treasure finds in Europe, and Rendlesham, possibly the court of its probable royal occupants, the Wuffingas.

From the watery expanses either side of me, I could hear the mewing, peeping calls of sandpipers and snipes. Marshes like these are home to other, more elusive, species too: otters, foxes, eels and booming bitterns. A pre-Conquest imagination might have added giants, bears, demons, wolves and sea-monsters. The Exeter Book poem of wisdom verses called *Maxims II* tells us that 'the giant must dwell in the fen, alone in the land'. Likewise, in the Old English epic *Beowulf*, Grendel and Grendel's mother occupy underwater caves in the fens beyond Heorot, the hall, and demonic spirits live in the fenland barrow St Guthlac chooses for his hermitage. As scholar of Old English poetry Jennifer Neville points out, the dark forces of the fens and other wild places need not be sorted into 'natural' and 'supernatural'; they were all threats to society's survival. 'They are not outside of nature,' she writes, 'but rather outside of human knowledge and control.'

Between the Sutton Hoo ship burial, dated to the early seventh century, and the making of the Exeter Book in the late tenth, a society made up of separate warring kingdoms coalesced into a more unified whole and began calling itself 'English'. Much had changed, but some tendencies remained. A fascination with visual and verbal riddles is one.

Art that we associate with early medieval Germanic cultures, including that of the Sutton Hoo ship burial, is full of interlacing serpentine creatures, birds and vines. The term *horor vacui* ('fear of the empty') denotes busy images with no blank space. You can see a dazzling example in Gallery 41 of the British Museum: the golden Sutton Hoo belt buckle. In a not-quite-symmetrical pattern, thirteen interlacing beasts, raptors and snakes, all with long, lacertine bodies, race, writhing, around three raised gold bosses. The level of detail is such that lines of embossed beading adorn the skin of the outer interlacing creatures, the grooves stained black with a mixture called niello, while punched, niello-filled dots decorate the inner creatures' skin. Contrast and contour animate the gold surface, creating an effect that is not only beautiful, but literally amazing.

In many cultures, knot-work has an apotropaic function. That is to say, it serves to repel malevolent forces. It decorates, along with the snarling heads of beasts and dragons, everything from medieval books and battle helmets to doors and the prows of ships. At the same time, we might see these forms of ornament as the visual sibling to the carefully crafted Old English riddles of the Exeter Book, as well as the elegies buried among them of which *Wulf and Eadwacer* is one. They reflect a culture that enjoyed discerning meaning through visual and verbal play.

The Sutton Hoo ship burial took place around the time that Christian missionaries from Ireland and Rome took the English in a two-pronged conversion, via Iona and Kent. In the subsequent centuries, we see art being produced that combines Celtic, Germanic, Italian and Middle Eastern traditions. One Christian import that would have appealed to the riddling Germanic mindset is a technique for reading Scripture called *exegesis*. The word brings together the Greek *ex-* (meaning: 'out') and *hegeisthai* (meaning: 'to lead/guide'). Christians, especially monks and nuns, were taught to tease out the many-layered, intertwining meanings of religious texts through reading and contemplation. As we have seen from the previous chapter, this interpretative mindset extended beyond Scripture, to the other great example of divine handiwork: Creation. You sense the intrigue it generated in *Wulf and Eadwacer*, the other Old English elegies, and their neighbouring riddles.

I turned tail on my muddy ridge and picked my way out of the reed bed. From there I travelled to

Chapter Six

Catastrophe

Portents and Parchment

I saw a purple cloth covering an altar. Then, as I drew closer, I saw it pouring onto the floor and realised it was not, after all, a cloth, but purple blood flowing from the neck of a priest who lay dead on the altar. The chalice was still in his hand and the wafer beside it, soaking up the blood. For the rest of the night I slept fitfully, wishing the darkness away.

It was not the first omen. During the stormy winter just gone we saw bright sheets of light flashing over the sky, whirling winds and a dragon spewing flames, reflected a thousand times in the shattered sea. And spring brought kinder weather, but by then the cattle had died of exposure and the blossom had been blown from the trees. All across the land, people starved.

It is summer now and I know a fresh ordeal is coming, but today the wind is fair and the sun is on my face. During the hours in the workshop, I can blot out the dream of the altar and the slaughtered priest. Here, I am surrounded by my brothers, whose mellow industry charges the silent air: steady breaths, a suppressed cough, the creak of a stool, the flick of a pen-knife against a nib, over the rhythmic hush of the harbour below and the tides that divide us from the mainland.

It being five days before the Ides of June, the sun rises early and goes late to bed. We work likewise. On days like these I used to complain to myself about the ache in my back and shoulder, the tedium of working and praying beside the same faces with their predictable, sometimes reprehensible habits, but today I can bear it. I have suffered, I have had patience; for His name's sake I have laboured. If the omens portend Judgement Day, the coming of Alpha and Omega, with his hair white like wool, eyes of flame and voice of many waters, I am grateful for the distraction.

Arranged so as to receive the most light from the windows, pages of unblemished parchment lie on the tilted desks. They are scored with lines and ready for text. With open books serving as our guides, we do as Scripture instructs us; we dip our pens – once the joy of birds – into horns of black ink and inscribe the letters, stroke by careful stroke. Some of us have trays of oyster shells, cups for brilliant pigments of orpiment, verdigris and purple. It has taken each of us many years of regulated practice, interspersed with prayer in the chapel, to be permitted to copy Scripture, though none of us will ever be worthy.

One hundred years ago, brothers at our Priory made a Gospel Book that surpasses any other made by human hands. Treasure-bound, it lies on the shrine of our very own St Cuthbert, beside the high altar. Its fine jet-black letters fill the pages, and intricately arranged birds and beasts animate its great initials, pigmented, like marble, in many hues. The gleaming Gospel Book is a treasure of all kinds: in the sanctity of its text, in the quality of its artistry and in the gold and jewels of its binding. All these things remind us of our inheritance as brothers of Holy Island and the responsibility we hold to God. We ask the Gospel Book's makers – Eadfrith, Athelwold and Billfrith the Anchorite – to intercede for our souls.

I was shown the book once, after the winter storms, when I had gone to see the Prior to tell him about my visions and the signs in the sky, about my sense of great foreboding. He opened it on the page of our Lord's Incarnation. The letters of the reading filled the parchment, their bodies packed with intertwining birds, painted in shades of purple. He spoke the words of a Psalm:

'Behold how good and how pleasant it is for brethren to dwell in unity.'

I told him I did not understand.

'We are like these birds, dwelling together in the Word of God,' he said, pointing to the letter full of winding necks and folded wings. 'If doom approaches, what would we do differently?'

I had considered the beauty of the page and the care of those who had made it.

'I don't want any other life,' I replied.

A bell rings for Sext and I am roused from my memories back to the evening light of the workshop. We set down our pens and pen-knives and leave by the south door to walk across the precinct to the Chapel. I look out over the sea, but my gaze snags on something I cannot at first interpret. Why are the fishermen out so late in the day? I look harder. No. These are not the familiar vessels now floating in the harbour, raised up by the tide. These are larger, much larger, and driving through the water, dragon-prowed, square-sailed, sailing towards us.

'Ships,' is all I can say to my brothers. Men are moving on the decks, axes in their hands.

In my mind's eye: whirlwinds, flames and dragons on the waves. An altar running with blood.

In 793, Britain's weather foreshadowed catastrophe. The entry for that year in the *Anglo-Saxon Chronicles* tells us, 'Here terrible portents came about over the land of Northumbria, and miserably frightened the people: these were immense flashes of lightning, and fiery dragons were seen flying in the air. A great famine immediately followed these signs.' What came next shocked Christendom: 'and a little after that in the same year on the 8 [June] the raiding of heathen men miserably devastated God's church in Lindisfarne island by looting and slaughter.'

When Lindisfarne was attacked, news reached Alcuin of York, an English scholar working in the court of Charlemagne in Aachen. He wrote a commiserating letter to the Bishop of Lindisfarne, lamenting how the attackers had 'poured out the blood of saints around the altar, laid waste to the house of our hope, trampled on the bodies of saints in the temple of God like dung in the street' and wondering how it could be that the monastery's homegrown Saint Cuthbert had not averted this catastrophe.

Alcuin's language is reminiscent of that found in the sixth-century *The Ruin of Britain*, by British cleric, Gildas. Referring to English seizure of lands long held by the Britons, he writes, 'in the midst of the streets lay the tops of lofty towers, tumbled to the ground, stones of high walls, holy altars, fragments of human bodies, covered with livid clots of coagulated blood, looking as if they had been squeezed together in a press; and with no chance of being buried, save in the ruins of the houses, or in the ravening bellies of wild beasts and birds.' In only a few centuries, the English, whose arrival had inspired such words, would themselves feel the cruelty of invasion, and the language of sacrilege would once again serve to condemn an enemy from across the sea.

To live in early medieval Britain was to be surrounded by evidence of fallen civilisation. Roman occupation had filled the landscape with monumental stone buildings, temples, walls, roads and cultivated farmland, but with the official withdrawal of its administration in 410 CE, the stream of imperial wealth ran dry, handsome roads and walls were neglected, frost burst rocks and plants forced open cracks. Many cities, including London, were all but abandoned.

In the Exeter Book, the narrator of a poem known as The Ruin describes walking through a derelict city of Roman grandeur. There are bath-houses that once rang with song. There are walls worthy of the handiwork of giants standing open to the elements. The Ruin ponders the theme of earthly transience central to other Old English elegies, but this time by means of the material evidence of political collapse.

The Ruin explores ideas that came to early medieval thought in the work of the late antique philosopher Boethius. In his Consolation of Philosophy, the narrator speaks from a prison cell to a personification of

Wisdom. Out of this dialogue emerged the power-ful image of the Wheel of Fortune. The unwise soul clings to its outer rim and falls furthest when the wheel turns. The wise soul, on the other hand, resides close to the hub, the home of God, and is no longer Fortune's plaything.

Given their philosophical subtext, we should guard against too literal a reading of any of these poems. *The Ruin* is not an eye-witness description of a specific crumbling Roman city in a post-Roman world. What *The Ruin* really prefigures is the ultimate ruination of *all* earthly kingdoms with the coming of the Kingdom of Heaven. So too the monks of Lindisfarne would have known that their home would one day crumble, perhaps they thought that day not very far away.

To the medieval Christian mind, fires, famines, storms and whirlwinds were a feature of a postlapsarian world, a world, that is, in which humans had fallen from the state of innocence they had enjoyed in Eden, into a state of perpetual peril. In the Exeter Book poem *The Phoenix*, the narrator describes the bird's distant, perfect home, as having no 'rain nor snow, nor breath of frost nor scorch of fire, nor falling of hail, nor drizzle of rime, nor heat of the sun nor incessant cold, nor torrid weather, nor wintry shower'. The unusual clemency of this landscape's climate is implicitly attributed to its distance from humanity: 'this expanse of land is not accessible to the many potentates across the world . . . it is far removed from evil-doers.' It is a place untouched by sadness, disease and death.

And bad weather was not just a temporary concern. The biblical Book of the Apocalypse, as it was known then, promised that omens in the sky and tumultuous weather would precede Doomsday (dōm is the Old English word for 'judgement'). As the poem prosaically known as *Judgement Day II* puts it:

> All of terra firma will tremble,
> the mountains will tumble and melt,
> the hillsides soften and sag
> and the terrible shriek of the turbulent sea
> will utterly unhinge the minds of all men.
> So, too, the sky above will be

black and benighted, completely blocked out,
darkened and dim, as swarthy as silva.
The stars will work loose from their fixings, and fall,
and the morning sun will be instantly inky.
The moon will have nowhere near the might
it needs to put night's darkness to flight.
Signs signalling death will descend from above,

Even before the Viking raid, the monks of Lindisfarne are likely to have believed, as Bede believed, that they were living in the sixth and final age of the world, an age that would see the Apocalypse. The early Middle Ages happened to be a time of especially cold and stormy weather for north-west Europe, so, by their own measure of the world, they had as much reason as we do to fear extreme climatic conditions. The proximity of Judgement Day kept mortality in the forefront of the imagination.

But there was hope. If his letters are anything to go by, Alcuin was a firm believer in the virtues of brotherly love. A quotation from one of his letters reads, 'Alas, if only it were granted to me . . . to be transported to you, how I would sink into your embrace . . . how I would cover, with tightly pressed lips, not only your eyes, ears and mouth, but also your every finger and your toes, not once but many times.'

While these lines make for odd reading today, given Alcuin's monastic celibacy, what we can infer with some confidence is that monasteries were places in which the existential benefit of communal living and mutual succour suffused the language of everyday life. In the ninth-century Irish text *The Voyage of St Brendan the Abbot*, Brendan sets sail with a group of fellow monks and wanders the ocean for seven years. Each year they visit the same group of islands, including, at Easter, an island inhabited by a huge flock of birds, perched in a mighty tree and singing. Among the lines of Scripture recited in their song is Psalm 133, 'Behold how good and how pleasant it is for brethren to dwell in unity.' The birds tell Brendan they are fallen angels, biding their time on earth, until they can return to heaven. They make an interesting parallel to the monks themselves.

If you enter into the sanctuary that is the Treasures Gallery of the British Library, you are likely to find a manuscript called the Lindisfarne Gospels, displayed to showcase one of its lavishly decorated openings. Made by a group of monks at Lindisfarne, then, a century later, carried to Chester-le-Street, along with St Cuthbert's body, by monks who had fled the Viking attack, it is a testament to the community's commitment to craft in the knowledge of the inevitability of death. Ornate initials unwind across its decorated pages, filled with the interlacing forms of highly stylised birds. The art of the Lindisfarne Gospels, which translates ancient Celtic and Germanic metalwork designs into the imported medium of paint on parchment, is mesmerising, born of an environment that placed value on lovingly crafted work *because* of the threat of doom, not in spite of it. It is the art of this manuscript, and its production context, that inspired the story you have just read.

The pillboxes that stud the otherwise wild coast around Lindisfarne attest to England's most recent fear of attack by warriors from across the sea. I sat on one to eat my lunch, having joined friends for the last two days of a hike from Melrose, following the Cuthbert Way. From where we sat, we could see Holy Island and the ruins of Lindisfarne Priory, which, like those of Whitby Abbey, are all gothic crags and pinnacles, built on the site of an earlier foundation.

From my place on the pillbox, I thought how the ruins across the expanse, flooded several times a day by the tides, had once been a hive of activity, a community with ties to Iona and Ireland, and from there to the asceticism of the Egyptian desert fathers. Yet, for all its connections, the original foundation would have been remote and vulnerable.

Leaving the grassy coast, we began the walk across the mudflats, now revealed by the ebbing tide, to Holy Island. The wind bowed our heads into submission, so that my sharpest memory of the walk consists of the sight of innumerable worm-holes in the sand passing beneath my narrowed eyes. On the island, the ruins themselves appear sculpted, all sockets and eggs on the surface in the sandstone, scooped out and smoothed by the relentless wind. When he was alive in the mid-seventh century, St Cuthbert lived further out to sea on one of the Farne Islands and was said to stand in the seawater, praying, no matter how tempestuous the weather.

We have encountered the term 'ascetic' already when discussing hermits and Irish monasticism. Its Greek root, *askesis*, means 'exercise'. Discussing the medieval impulse to find a balance between the wild and the dead (by means of tempering or finding temperance), art historian Paul Binski has noted that *askesis* did not necessarily mean commitment to an extreme life alone in the wilderness, like the one chosen by Cuthbert. It could also mean the lifestyle like the one lived by the monks who remained on Holy Island, Lindisfarne, which involved daily exercises in self-discipline. Craft was such an exercise; the most prestigious books demanded the most laborious scripts, capital letters for which the scribe would have to constantly lift and rotate the pen, with little wedges beginning and terminating each stroke. And that is only the writing. In just one small section of the initial page for Luke's Gospel in the Lindisfarne Gospels, British Library analysis counted 1,939 decorative red dots. Whether or not the ornament was the work of a single artist, the manuscript represents a fastidious collaboration made in the consciousness of mortality, even impending doom. It represents an active demonstration that the Christian message had spread even as far as this remote archipelago on the edge of the great gaping ocean, that it might not be forgotten on Judgement Day. Perhaps it could be said that the Lindisfarne Gospels represent a form of medieval activism, a refusal to be overwhelmed by the terrors of the world. I have sometimes wondered whether early monastic viewers beheld the Lindisfarne Gospels' interlacing birds and recalled the Psalm sung by the birds in *The Voyage of St Brendan*: 'Behold how good and how pleasant it is for brethren to dwell in unity.' Of course, the birds in the decorated initial do not sing the Word of God, but entwine, as if dancing, within it. Either way, they reflect the daily exertion to nudge the suspended elements of life – the spiritual ecosystem, so easily out of temper – into something resembling harmony, their earthly exertion for the sake of salvation.

Chapter Seven

Paradise

The Message in the Sand

Docking at the harbour with a boatload of treasure will always draw a crowd. It was said that the monks had been away for years and had discovered an earthly paradise. I thought about staying to listen to what they had to say but I hardly believed them and I had seen enough treasure for a lifetime. For me it was tainted with the onion-ripe smell of his body; the duty to taste the boneless hilt beside the garnet-encrusted one, the worm beside the serpent-patterned steel with which he drove my family away.

I looked down and my eye lighted on the piece of wood, just as though the sea had placed it there for me to find. As I looked closer, picking it up, I discerned a scent of spices. Images rose to my mind of trees heavy with fruit, their trunks encircled by herbs. Brushing the sand from the grain, I saw that the panel, the size and shape of a walnut leaf, bore a message in runes. They were fine and picked out in various colours. I took myself away from the throng to read. As I read my heart started to hammer in my chest and my body began to sway.

It was a summons, washed up at my feet after too many years of silence, solid and real in my hand. I would answer its message, whatever the cost. I tucked the piece of wood into my clothes and hastened back to the hall, leaving the crowd on the beach gaping at the boat full of treasure.

That night I served with the other women at the feast, and for the first time in years my mood was lifted out of mourning. According to the message, I was tasked to wait for the signal, so the next day I stole away from the hall and walked to the clifftop. I waited but heard nothing, knowing it was still too early in the year. I returned to the clifftop every day for a month till at last it came. There, with the sea before me and the blossom-bordered forest behind, it rang out just as the message had said, the call of a cuckoo, the herald of summer. Energy flooded my limbs as the dawn broke through the eastern windows. I crept back to the hall, kissed my friends' sleeping heads, kept my eyes from the wine-soaked mass of my oppressor, and took a travelling cloak from one of the benches. From there I hurried to the harbour, stole a hide-covered boat and prayed that no one had seen me leave.

Once out of sight of land, I read the piece of wood again. The message told me that it had come to me by boat and had been inscribed by one with whom I had made vows in former days. The message asked me to remember back to before the invasion, when I had lived with him as a family, surrounded by the homes of our friends, and all had been well. Of course. I had recalled them every day of my service to a warlord, though the memories pained me too much to picture them clearly.

This is what the message told me. My beloved

(whom I had thought was dead) was alive. The voice of the grain told me that, after I was taken, he had escaped the onslaught, had tried to find me, had hoped to rescue me from the conquering army, but had been forced to flee. He promised himself he would not leave me in that place, but with nowhere safe to bring me, he had sailed south to a land where he had built a new hall and grown rich in bossed circlets and burnished gold. But all the while, no happiness was possible without me by his side. Set sail, he said, and let no one living deter you on your journey! He gave me the runes: Sun and Heaven, Grave and Joy, and Human to guide me on my way.

With his message in my fist, I sailed from my captors and put my faith in the sea, but the journey proved long and difficult. I set sail seven years ago and still I have not found him nor the homeland he described.

Every year of these seven years, I have come upon the same islands, each one in turn. On the first island is a crystal monastery, where the brothers keep a vow of silence. The first time I went there, they gave me food and frowned when I tried to ask them where I might find my beloved. Now they leave me a basket of food on the beach. I am sorry, because their company would have been welcome, but at least I could eat.

Another island is covered in sheep the size of cows, with copious white wool that I gathered to use as a mattress. The sheep are very tame, and on my third year travelling around these islands, I killed one by hitting its head with a rock. What meat I didn't eat fresh I cured in brine and hung from the mast of my boat. It was nourishing food, but when I have visited the island since, I have felt terrible guilt and gathered the wool like a thief in the night.

Yet another island is covered with vines so lush I could live off the juice of one grape for three days. I remember biting through the skin, feeling it crack under the pressure of my teeth and tasting its sweet flesh. Overjoyed, I filled my boat with so many grapes I could hardly row or see the horizon, but after a month their sweetness cloyed and when they did finally begin to rot, the odour of rancid grape exuded from my skin and clung to the back of my mouth. This year, after seven years, I took only enough grapes for a week and accepted the hunger that followed.

The worst of the islands is not an island at all, but a whale. I learned to stay in the boat when I arrived there. It was only by luck, on my first visit, that I had gone back to the boat for bedding when the creature – a great whale – began to dive. If I had remained on its back I would be a corpse, floating in the abyss.

The boat was my refuge for the islands that spew fire and ice too, especially as, on Sundays, the Island of Ice is the home of Judas Iscariot. He said God puts him there each Sunday as respite from the torments of hell. He did not seem dangerous, so I often lingered nearby and allowed myself a moment of his company, but it did disturb me how he relished the feeling of the bitter winds on his face and the freezing ocean on his bare, pimpled skin. I imagined hell to be a very terrible place for such tortures to count as comfort.

Each year Judas asked me to stay and keep him company, and each year I refused. But I cannot say I was not finding it more and more difficult to turn myself away from his beseeching, frost-lashed eyes. I was worried that next time I would give in. To be with anyone, even a traitor, would be better than endless solitude, and Judas was in need of comfort. I clutched the wooden panel in my hand for strength.

I was becoming so lonely but Easter was a relief. This was the day on which the wind took me to the Island of Birds and held me just off shore. It was small, with a huge fountain at the centre and a mighty tree growing above the fountain. The tree is not tall, but extended a long way in either direction, to the point of overhanging the cliffs at the island's edge. At first I thought its leaves, unnaturally white, were moving, but then I saw that it was covered in so many birds that they obscured branch and bough.

When I first arrived at the island, the birds were all singing as one. I had wished I knew the words to the song, for it was very beautiful: sad and joyful at the same time, full of kindness, intelligence and sorrow. I stood in my little boat and called out to them, asking who they were. One of them took off from the tree, and as it flew its wings rang with bells. Landing on the prow, it told me their story.

'At the very dawn of time,' said the bird, 'we were angels. But when Lucifer fell, he dragged us with him. Somehow, in that great tumult, we lost our places in heaven.'

Leaning forward on the lilting waves, I was amazed and asked, 'Why then, are you not in hell, with the other fallen angels and Lucifer himself?'

'Because we do not deserve to suffer. For the rest of the year, we are like other exiled spirits, inhabiting the earth or wandering the sky, but on Holy Days, like Easter, we are able to take the shape of birds, gather together, and sing.'

I stood alone in my little boat as the bird flew back to the tree, reflected in the calm water, wings chiming, and began singing with all the rest. As I watched and listened, I tried to hold portions of the melody in my head and remember the words. I imagined myself singing them to my beloved when I found him at last, but when the day came to an end I had memorised only a few notes. As the wind pushed me away from the island, the birds stopped singing and took flight with the whooshing sound of a waterfall flowing upside down. I watched them spiral and twist into the sunset, making letter shapes in the sky. For all my travels over the next year, I longed for the Island of Birds almost as much as I longed for my beloved.

Each Easter, I saw the birds again and learned a bit more of their song, which brought me some happiness. It was the only thing to distract me from despondency and my growing doubt that I would ever reach my destination. As my seventh Easter at sea approached, I anticipated the Island of Birds like never before. I was beginning to forget my reason for this journey; in earlier years I used to read the wooden panel constantly, its grain familiar against my palm, but now it lay in the bottom of the boat, bleaching in the sun.

It was Easter morning, a gentle, salt-laced breeze

had risen fully, had reached the perfection of Easter, the voices radiated, like the notes of a lyre, countless times over, diverging into harmonies, my own higher tones finding their place above the cascade of deeper voices, some so deep they seemed to sound the very ocean. Tears spilled from my eyes, and though I could see from the blurred edges of my vision that fishes were circling my boat, nose to tail, I wondered with all my sense, but I did not look. I must sing and listen, one with the great circles of the universe. I must not think of anything.

We were still singing as the sun began to descend. Then the harmonious voices converged. The sun was sliding low over the sea, its reflection melting towards me and the birds rushing from their branches, whooshing to form great letters in the sky, leaving me behind. I cried after them, loneliness flooding into the void left by their song.

'I belong with you! Please let me come with you!'

The angelic flock did not answer, not even the bird that first spoke to me from the prow. They receded from sight, fading to a scattering of dots on the horizon. Then they were gone, and I was standing alone before the island and its bare-boughed tree, my hands empty.

I sat down and put my head on my knees, the great vastness of the ocean seeming to yawn on every side. I was so tired and so alone. I could not go through it all over again. Not another year. Not the crystal monastery, the grapes, the sheep, the whale and the isle of Judas Iscariot. I imagined cutting a hole in the hide of my boat and letting it fill with water.

I remembered the words of the message. 'Let no one living deter you on your journey.' No one living. I am living. Will I be my greatest obstacle? Opening my eyes, I noticed the piece of wood on the floor. Swimming in my view was the part that I had never understood, the runes to help me on my way: Sun and Heaven, Grave and Joy, and Human. *Is this the Grave?* I think, for what is despair if not death? The Sun, that was Easter, surely. The birds, the singing, then, that must have been a glimpse of Heaven. Something stirred in my heart. After the grave comes Joy and after that, Human. I am Human. I seek Human. There was hope. I picked up my oars. I had to carry on.

Noticing that the wind had changed direction, I looked ahead and was able to discern, over the rippling waves, a dark mist stretching as far as the eye could see. The mist was new, I had never seen it before. I had to go towards it. Seized with sudden fear that it would vanish, I struck out for the darkness, and though I did not know if it would lead me into peril, I did know that to ignore it would be to submit to despair. For that sole reason I could not let the mist get away.

The sun set fully and I dragged my oars through the water to the place where I had last seen the fog. I wondered if it had vanished, and my heart tightened with anguish. But then the air changed. My hair became damp and beads of moisture covered my skin. I had reached and entered the mist: I had made it, whatever followed.

For a long while, perhaps the length of a night, I journeyed through the cloud. My arms were tired but I did not put down the oars. I sang the birds' song to keep myself awake, though my quiet voice got nowhere in the thick vapour and wrapped about my head. I could see nothing until dawn approached. Then I could make out the water lapping against the sides of the boat, but no further.

As the time, the water and the vapour passed, I thought back to the monks whose vessel, I supposed, had brought me the message that had sent me on this journey. They had found an earthly paradise, or so the crowd had whispered. Could it be that this very paradise lay on the other side of the mist? In my mind, I saw the fog lift like eyelids. My skin still damp, I found myself looking across clear blue water to a high plateau, shining by the light of a new sunrise. A river wound from the centre of the plateau, flanked by trees heavy with fruit and cloaked with luminous leaves, domed over by a crystal sky. I imagined myself breathing in the air and was reminded by its cold, earthy sweetness of the first days of spring after a long winter. As my vessel crunched onto the sand, I saw that the pebbles left in drifts by the surf were precious gems, displaying all the colours I had ever seen and yet more besides. I grasped my only possession, the faded wooden message that called me to this quest, and climbed out of the beach.

As I saw myself walking inland I beheld more wondrous sights. A huge cat with fur like the plumage of a kingfisher watched me from a cave, all benevolence and beauty, lifting its liquid eyes as a bird flew overhead, her crested head and neck shimmering, green-cloaked and shot through with purple hues. I saw that her wings were white and her tail was gold and purple, covered in bright spots. I followed her, still treading gems beneath my feet, then the stems of grasses, until she landed in the top of a tree, fixing me with an eye like a fiery stone set in gold. I saw that her nest was made of herbs and woodland flowers – lemon balm, woodland star, salvia and orchids – and with a shock of recognition, I discerned the scent of spices that had risen long ago from the wooden panel, first lifted from the sand.

Expectation urged me on. In this wilderness, there was no path for me to follow and yet I imagined knowing exactly where to tread. I moved through the ferns and tree-trunks, my path wandered by bees, clutching their flower loot, until lower shrubs and grasses once again replaced the forest and I reached the edge of a river, full of fish, trailing weeds and the light glancing from the backs of basking insects.

Then, as if no time had passed, as if I had not been wandering for seven long years and stood at the very brink of despair, as if we had not been separated by war, slavery and exile, I saw him. He stood on the opposite bank.

Over his shoulder I could see a village around a high-gabled hall, ridged with flowering vines. I saw our children gathered under its eaves.

'We knew you'd find us,' he said. 'Come across the river.'

A terrestrial paradise existed somewhere in the world. As much could be inferred from the account of Eden in the Old Testament Book of Genesis, as well as contemporary descriptions that an educated early medieval Christian might have encountered. Take, for instance, the portrayal of such a region by the narrator of the Old English Exeter Book poem, *The Phoenix*:

> That illustrious land
> is brimming with blossoms. No mountains or bluffs
> climb steeply there; nor do rocky cliffs
> loom high overhead like they do here.
> You'll find neither coombs or hollows or gulleys,
> barrows or boundary banks; no land that needs breaking
> lies around. Instead, that peerless plain
> thrives under the skies, thronged with joy.

What a fitting dwelling place for the phoenix, that, like Christ, was believed to rise again from the ashes of death. A very similar landscape is assigned to the iridescent protagonist of *The Panther*, which likewise serves as an allegory for Christ. This was a landscape held to be free from the unpleasantness of sin and hostile elements: impeccable and utterly abundant.

In the ninth-century Latin text *The Voyage of St Brendan the Abbot*, Brendan and his followers set sail on the ocean in search of just such a region. They leave the coast of Ireland in a hide-covered boat and surrender themselves, bravely, to the divinely directed currents of sea and sky. For seven years they wander the ocean, encountering the same curious sequence of islands each year at times that coincided with the events of the liturgical calendar. Over the course of the journey, three of the brothers who are less than holy are compelled to leave the company and, after seven years, the remainder find a dark mist: the way to the earthly paradise for which they had been searching. Mooring their boat on the shore of this supernal land, they meet a young man who invites them to pick as many fruits and gather as many precious stones as their boat can carry, so that they can return to their homeland to share the tale of their adventure.

While *The Voyage of St Brendan* was composed in Ireland, it sheds light on British cultures too. It was Irish missionaries, led by St Aidan, who spearheaded the conversion of the English in Northumbria and whose spirituality shaped its religious culture. The Irish, moreover, had close historical ties with the Welsh, as evidenced by, for instance, their linguistic relationship and the presence of ogham stones (monumental stones carved with a bespoke alphabet for Celtic languages) on both sides of the Irish Sea.

The Voyage of St Brendan is said to belong to a group of Old Irish texts known as *immrama*. They generally concern a hero's journey to the Otherworld. Thus, while the paradise sought by Brendan is not heaven, neither is it quite of the everyday land of sin and suffering where most humans live. In order to reach this paradisiacal region, he and his monks have to make a strange circuitous journey and be cleansed of sin. It has been suggested that their repetitive, seven-year, communal adventure and glimpse of paradise served as an allegory for the monastic life, while others have hypothesised that the story is based on a real-life journey across the Atlantic to North America. Whatever the case may be (and I lean towards the former), the text tells us that while a terrestrial paradise was believed to have existed, its accessibility depended not simply on your ability to make the physical journey, but also the condition of your soul.

Over the preceding pages, I have mentioned many of the Old English elegies of the Exeter Book and now we come to the last to be met here. It is traditionally known by the title *The Husband's Message*, and is narrated by a piece of wood bearing a message in runes. The message is directed to a woman and written by one who claims to have been her spouse in years gone by. They were separated by war, he says, and he forced to flee, while she remained subject to the conquerors. But he has found a way to reach her, now that he has established a new kingdom in a land to the south and can receive her as his queen:

> A feud drove him away
> from the victorious people. Now he himself has asked me
> to instruct you joyfully that you should stir up the water,
> after you have heard on the edge of the cliff
> the mournful cuckoo sing in the wood

The tone of the message is that of a love letter, but the content cryptic. The message offers a series of runes – ᚻ and ᚱ, ᛏ and ᛈ, and ᛗ, with the names Sun and Heaven, Grave and Joy, and Man (perhaps in the sense of 'Humanity', as in Modern English) – to help her on her way. *The Husband's Message* may be a riddle with a religious solution, perhaps aimed at a female monastic reader, but as with all the Old English elegies, it is beautiful whether or not it holds a higher allegorical meaning.

In this story, I have imagined the journey of the female recipient of the runic message. We never find out from the poem whether she answers his call. What if the southern land from which her husband writes is also the terrestrial paradise discovered by Brendan and his monks? On medieval world maps, Eden lies to the south-east of Britain and Ireland, so it's not too far off the mark.

We might infer of the narrator, if we read her story literally, that she is one of history's many women forced into sexual slavery. In *Beowulf*, the glittering wife of the great lord Hrothgar is called 'Wealtheow', which has been translated as 'foreign slave'. Wealtheow is afforded honour in the epic tale, but surely this was not the norm. One of the Exeter Book riddles is spoken from the perspective of an object wettened and swept 'within the blackness' by a 'dark-haired slave girl / brought far from Wales', 'some stupid drunken maidservant, on dark nights' who thrusts her 'wanton hand' on its breast and 'moves about frequently'. It is thought, from the wider context of the riddle, that the solution is leather, perhaps turned into a contraceptive or sexual device. But whatever the intended meaning of the riddle, hers is a story rarely preserved in the more formal chronicles. If you found her out on the waves, could you blame her for preferring to put her life in the hands of the sea than remain scorned and enslaved?

Of all the islands visited by Brendan, the one inhabited by a great flock of fallen angels in the guise of birds struck me as especially wonderful. Every winter, in wild lands all over Britain, starlings perform their murmurations. This year I visited a dawn murmuration on the Somerset Levels. I went quickly, anxious I would miss them, worried I already had. Except, once I got within a minute of their location, I realised I could hear the starlings singing with a noise like applause in a theatre. I got closer and saw a small group of early rising birdwatchers looking across one of the shallow lakes, towards a crescent of reeds.

Joining the birdwatchers, it took me a while to understand what I was seeing. Then I realised. The starlings were clinging in their thousands to the vertical stems of the reeds. They looked like black fly in a rose bush. I couldn't get my head round the sheer number of them, all singing together.

Then all at once the sound stopped, as if the curtain had lifted and the audience had fallen quiet. In a slow crescendo, a new sound began – like a wave, snow sliding from a roof, a rain-stick, or wind – and I saw that one part of the group of starlings had started to take off, to be followed by the rest of the group, more and more, a swarm rising into the air, louder and louder, reflected in the mirrored surface of the lake. The starlings became airborne in a long twisting ribbon. In his *Etymologies*, Isidore of Seville describes cranes flying in a letter formation, just as we see geese and seagulls flying now, but this was not a single letter, this was verse on the wing, tracing a path through the dawn.

The starlings cohered the ragged winter landscape; as if they represented the fundamental coherence of everything, however seemingly chaotic. Isidore of Seville also writes that birds are called '(*avis*) because they do not have set paths (*via*), but travel by means of pathless (*avia*) ways'. The Latin word for bird, *avis*, sounds similar to the Latin word for wilderness, *avium*, and so Isidore teases out an allegorical reading of a word by giving it a fictitious origin. To me, they made their own path. I wished I could inhabit that swarm, rise up into air with it, be swept along in the movement. When I came to read of the birds in the tree on the island before St Brendan, I imagined how it would feel to meet them in the pathless wilds of the ocean and how hard it would be to be left behind by that community if you wandered that wilderness alone.

What I envied in the birds was their absolute togetherness, a resolve that showed itself as a transient, beautiful harmony. It reminded me of my grand-mother's insistence that singing the Berlioz Requiem with two hundred others was 'better than sex and far less trouble'. It reminded me of dancing with a Lithuanian boy in freshers' week, who eschewed the solitary freestyle of our peers and swept me away in a kind of waltz that I barely kept up with. It reminded me of working an engraving block with my tools, excited to see an image coming into being, know-ing that with one slip of the hand, or cut too many, I would ruin everything. It reminded me of watching the members of a sports team find their rhythm and play as if reading each other's minds. In all these, harmony is as precarious as it is beautiful. Surely such moments are our terrestrial paradise breaking from deep waters – even the Abyss – like a pod of benevolent whales.

Appendix: The Exeter Book Reborn

*A selection of poems in Old and Modern English,
translated anew by George Younge*

I first met the Exeter Book as a student charged with translating *Wulf and Eadwacer*, one of several elegies to be found among the manuscript's riddles and other verses. The lines of that poem impressed my imagination like a watermark. I delighted in the relatability of the narrator's feelings and setting: as familiar as the rain she describes falling on her bowed shoulders. It fell on mine too as I cycled to lectures through the Autumn term.

This book looks further than Old English, towards precious portions of Middle Welsh and Insular Latin literature that helped shape each other (along with the literatures of other languages such as Old Norse and all-but-lost Pictish, though they were beyond the scope of these pages) in an age of intense cultural upheaval within Britain's shores. It mixes their motifs and celebrates their peculiarly insular, early medieval context. For that reason, this is a book about Britain, not England or English literature alone, and the Further Reading List given at the end invites readers to continue their own explorations into this multilingual era.

However, as *Wild* began with the Exeter Book, Dr George Younge, Lecturer in Medieval Literature at the University of York, has translated a selection of its verses to be offered here as an appendix. The translations reflect his technical knowledge of Old English and a sensitivity to the spirit of its poetry that will, I hope, bring readers into the urgent, thunderous, garnet-inlaid universe of the originals.

There are so many wonders to discover in this our transient world, however desiccated and dead they may seem to the disinterested eye. Our imaginations are to them like the fire to the phoenix; fixed in its flames, their hearts beat again and their colours gleam like an illuminated wing.

THE WIFE'S LAMENT

Ic þis giedd wrece bi me ful geomorre,
minre sylfre sið. Ic þæt secgan mæg,
hwæt ic yrmþa gebad, siþþan ic up weox,
niwes oþþe ealdes, no ma þonne nu.
A ic wite wonn minra wræcsiþa.

Ærest min hlaford gewat heonan of leodum
ofer yþa gelac; hæfde ic uhtceare
hwær min leodfruma londes wære.
Ða ic me feran gewat folgað secan,
wineleas wræcca, for minre weaþearfe.
Ongunnon þæt þæs monnes magas hycgan
þurh dyrne geþoht, þæt hy todælden unc,
þæt wit gewidost in woruldrice
lifdon laðlicost, ond mec longade.

Het mec hlaford min herheard niman,
ahte ic leofra lyt on þissum londstede,
holdra freonda. Forþon is min hyge geomor,
ða ic me ful gemæcne monnan funde,
heardsæligne, hygegeomorne,

THE WIFE'S LAMENT

I mouth this riddle of my melancholy,
the journey I took into myself. I'm free now to speak
of the crimes I've kept close since my coming of age:
the new wrongs, the old wrongs, the wrongs I still suffer,
always bearing my burden on the byways of hate.

First my man went from his men,
Over the play of the waves. For me, it was dread before dawn;
where in the world was my prince?
And so I set off in search of support,
cast out and alone for my woe and my want.
Then the plotting began: my man's kinsmen
with a furtive intent to split us in two
leaving lives stretched wide as the world,
and bile in the belly. Then the longing set in.

My prince ordered me here to this place—
not a great grove to find friends,
true friends, that is. And now my mind is melancholy,
since it turns out my most 'suitable' soulmate
was down on his luck, dark in his thoughts,

mod miþendne,   morþor hycgendne,
bliþe gebæro.   Ful oft wit beotedan
þæt unc ne gedælde   nemne deað ana
owiht elles;   eft is þæt onhworfen.
Is nu   swa hit no wære
freondscipe uncer.   Sceal ic feor ge neah
mines felaleofan   fæhðu dreogan.

    Heht mec mon wunian   on wuda bearwe,
under actreo   in þam eorðscræfe.
Eald is þes eorðsele,   eal ic eom oflongad.
Sindon dena dimme,   duna uphea,
bitre burgtunas,   brerum beweaxne:
wic wynna leas.   Ful oft mec her wraþe begeat
fromsiþ frean.   Frynd sind on eorþan,
leofe lifgende,   leger weardiað,
þonne ic on uhtan   ana gonge
under actreo   geond þas eorðscrafu.
Þær ic sittan mot   sumorlangne dæg,
þær ic wepan mæg   mine wræcsiþas,
earfoþa fela;   forþon ic æfre ne mæg
þære modceare   minre gerestan,
ne ealles þæs longaþes   þe mec on þissum life begeat.

    A scyle geong mon   wesan geomormod,
heard heortan geþoht,   swylce habban sceal

hiding a heart with murder in mind
behind an easy exterior. Many times we swore
only death could tear us apart —
that came back to bite me.
Now it's like it never happened,
our love. Wherever I am,
I pay the price for my prince's feud.

A man (who else) made this canopied clearing
my haunt: an earthen hollow at the heel of an oak.
Time's old in this soil-hall, makes me lost with longing.
Sunless fissures, looming hills,
brooding earthworks smothered by briars:
a place I call Sorrow. Often it seems
like I'm roughly restrained by my man
being gone. Elsewhere on earth
friends live their lives, make the most of their beds,
while I pace alone in a different dawn,
circling the chamber at the heel of the oak.
It's there that I sit all the summer-long day,
It's there I lament all the losses I've made
on the highways of hate. And so it goes,
and always will: no rest from my raging heart,
no rest from life's brutal longing.

May my sweet prince always be saddled with sadness,
bitter thoughts at his breast. Let him harbour heartbreak

bliþe gebæro,   eac þon breostceare,
sinsorgna gedreag,   sy æt him sylfum gelong
eal his worulde wyn,   sy ful wide fah
feorres folclondes,   þæt min freond siteð
under stanhliþe   storme behrimed,
wine werigmod,   wætre beflowen
on dreorsele.   Dreogeð se min wine
micle modceare;   he gemon to oft
wynlicran wic.   Wa bið þam þe sceal
of langoþe   leofes abidan.

behind those laidback looks,
a host of endless hurt. May his worldly gains
be his labour alone and his exile extend
to the tip of this territory, where he sits
at the heel of a cliff in a cloak made of cold by the wind —
my weary warrior surrounded by water,
in a chamber of gloom. There he'll suffer
the darkest depression as he dwells in his mind on
the place he calls Joy. Woe to those who
wait with longing for love.

Appendix

THE SEAFARER

Mæg ic be me sylfum   soðgied wrecan,
siþas secgan,   hu ic geswincdagum
earfoðhwile   oft þrowade,
bitre breostceare   gebiden hæbbe.
Gecunnad in ceole   cearselda fela,
atol yþa gewealc,   þær mec oft bigeat
nearo nihtwaco   æt nacan stefnan,
þonne he be clifum cnossað.   Calde geþrungen
wæron mine fet,   forste gebunden,
caldum clommum,   þær þa ceare seofedun
hat ymb heortan;   hungor innan slat
merewerges mod.   Þæt se mon ne wat
þe him on foldan   fægrost limpeð,
hu ic earmcearig   iscealdne sæ
winter wunade   wræccan lastum,
winemægum bidroren,
bihongen hrimgicelum;   hægl scurum fleag.
Þær ic ne gehyrde   butan hlimman sæ,
iscaldne wæg.   Hwilum ylfete song
dyde ic me to gomene,   ganetes hleoþor
ond huilpan sweg   fore hleahtor wera,

THE SEAFARER

Let me sing the song of my truth,
speak of the journey – how I often endured
backbreaking days and deep desperation,
sat with sharp sorrow at my chest.
I've taken in many pitiful places from my ship,
sickening sea swells. Often the nervous night watch
had me gripped at the bow of the boat
as it bottomed on the cliffs. The cold
crushed my feet, binding them in tingling
chains of frost, while griefs groaned
hot about my heart; inner hunger
savaged my seaworn soul.
No light-hearted landlubber
can know what I went through that winter:
sorrowful on the ice-cold sea and the paths of exile,
deprived of dear kinsmen,
draped in icicles, hammered by hail.
Out there, I'd hear nothing but the roar of the ocean,
and the shivering wave. Sometimes
I'd imagine the swan sang a song for me. The gannet's cry
and the curlew's shriek became the laughter of men;

mæw singende   fore medodrince.
Stormas þær stanclifu beotan,   þær him stearn oncwæð
isigfeþera;   ful oft þæt earn bigeal,
urigfeþra;   ne ænig hleomæga
feasceaftig ferð   frefran meahte.

Forþon him gelyfeð lyt,   se þe ah lifes wyn
gebiden in burgum,   bealosiþa hwon,
wlonc ond wingal,   hu ic werig oft
in brimlade   bidan sceolde.
Nap nihtscua,   norþan sniwde,
hrim hrusan bond,   hægl feol on eorþan,
corna caldast.   Forþon cnyssað nu
heortan geþohtas,   þæt ic hean streamas,
sealtyþa gelac   sylf cunnige;
monað modes lust   mæla gehwylce
ferð to feran,   þæt ic feor heonan
elþeodigra   eard gesece.
Forþon nis þæs modwlonc   mon ofer eorþan,
ne his gifena þæs god,   ne in geoguþe to þæs hwæt,
ne in his dædum to þæs deor,   ne him his dryhten to þæs hold,
þæt he a his sæfore   sorge næbbe,
to hwon hine dryhten   gedon wille.
Ne biþ him to hearpan hyge   ne to hringþege,
ne to wife wyn   ne to worulde hyht,

the sea-mew's singing was the hum of the mead-hall.
Storms beat the cliffs and the icy-feathered tern
answered back. Now and then, the sea eagle had his say,
feathers wet with spray. No kinsmen
could console my empty soul.

Those who've had all of life's comforts —
safe in their cities, spared dangerous journeys,
flushed with their pride and their wine — how can they comprehend
what it meant when I made my weary way on the sea-lane?
Night's shadow would bring darkness and the northerlies snow,
frost gripped the ground and hail hit the earth,
the coldest of grains. Even so, the thoughts of my heart
gnaw at me now to test myself further
on the cold currents and the salty swells.
Over and over, the soul's yearning urges
my spirit to set forth, so that far from here
I might seek out some land of strangers.
I know of no man on earth so sure of his mind,
so quick in his gifts, hot-headed in youth,
daring in deeds, or popular with his peers,
that he wouldn't have worries on his voyage
about what the Lord has in store for him.
He'll have no thought for the harp, the receiving of rings,
a woman's caress, dreams of the future,

ne ymbe owiht elles,   nefne ymb yða gewealc,
ac a hafað longunge   se þe on lagu fundað.

Bearwas blostmum nimað,   byrig fægriað,
wongas wlitigiað,   woruld onetteð;
ealle þa gemoniað   modes fusne
sefan to siþe,   þam þe swa þenceð
on flodwegas   feor gewitan.
Swylce geac monað   geomran reorde,
singeð sumeres weard,   sorge beodeð
bitter in breosthord.   Þæt se beorn ne wat,
esteadig secg,   hwæt þa sume dreogað
þe þa wræclastas   widost lecgað.

Forþon nu min hyge hweorfeð   ofer hreþerlocan,
min modsefa   mid mereflode
ofer hwæles eþel   hweorfeð wide,
eorþan sceatas,   cymeð eft to me
gifre ond grædig,   gielleð anfloga,
hweteð on hwælweg   hreþer unwearnum
ofer holma gelagu.   Forþon me hatran sind
dryhtnes dreamas   þonne þis deade lif,
læne on londe.   Ic gelyfe no
þæt him eorðwelan   ece stondað.
Simle þreora sum   þinga gehwylce,
ær his tidege,   to tweon weorþeð;

or anything else – in the end, it's the surging of waves.
Once you've tasted the sea, there's always the longing.

Woods break into blossom, towns beautify,
meadows shimmer and the world wakes up.
Transforming spring tugs at the conscience
of the man minded to the journey, he who intends
to travel far on the floodways.
The cuckoo forewarns with its melancholy cry;
the summer watchman sings, predicting pain
with a heavy heart. Those who have it easy
will never know what some people suffer
when they follow their exile to its furthest extent.

And so my spirit roams beyond the heart's restraints.
My mind casts off on the swollen sea,
eddies freely in the whale's wake,
spins to the edges of the earth, then returns to me,
restless and ravenous. Again, the lonely flier cries,
prompting my powerless heart back to the way of the whale,
onto the sweep of the sea. You see, God's ecstasies
are more intense for me than this dead life
we're loaned on land; I've got no faith
that mechanical man can stand time's test.
Whoever they are, one of three things
will press on a person when their number is up:

adl oþþe yldo   oþþe ecghete
fægum fromweardum   feorh oðþringeð.
Forþon bið eorla gehwam   æftercweþendra
lof lifgendra   lastworda betst,
þæt he gewyrce,   ær he on weg scyle,
fremman on foldan   wið feonda niþ,
deorum dædum   deofle togeanes,
þæt hine ælda bearn   æfter hergen,
ond his lof siþþan   lifge mid englum
awa to ealdre,   ecan lifes blæd,
dream mid dugeþum.   Dagas sind gewitene,
ealle onmedlan   eorþan rices;
næron nu cyningas   ne caseras
ne goldgiefan   swylce iu wæron,
þonne hi mæst mid him   mærþa gefremedon
ond on dryhtlicestum   dome lifdon.
Gedroren is þeos duguð eal,   dreamas sind gewitene,
wuniað þa wacran   ond þas woruld healdaþ,
brucað þurh bisgo.   Blæd is gehnæged,
eorþan indryhto   ealdað ond searað,
swa nu monna gehwylc   geond middangeard.
Yldo him on fareð,   onsyn blacað,
gomelfeax gnornað,   wat his iuwine,
æþelinga bearn,   eorþan forgiefene.
Ne mæg him þonne se flæschoma,   þonne him þæt feorg losað,
ne swete forswelgan   ne sar gefelan,

illness, age, or the edge of the sword —
which of these three will squeeze breath from the body?
For all of us, then, it's the praise of the living,
acclaim of the after-comer, that's the strongest impression
we can make before taking our way.
For our actions on earth against the evil of enemies,
daring deeds in the face of the devil,
the next generation honours us afterwards,
and our glory lives on with the angels,
always unbending in splendour neverending
entranced with the heavenly troop. Gone are the days
when nations made sense;
gone are the kings and the emperors,
the gold-givers of yester-year
who performed for themselves
all those memorable deeds, living in lordly renown.
Their whole system has ceased, the consensus collapsed,
now only the craven carry on. It's they who've inherited the earth,
and with it the profits of pain. The flame's flickered out.
Earth's essence decays and dries up,
and with it the life of each man in the land.
Old Greybeard grieves as age overtakes him,
his skin growing sheer as he thinks on his friends,
the children of princes, now gifts for the grave.
When his spirit slips away, that suit of skin
won't sense sweetness or pain,

ne hond onhreran   ne mid hyge þencan.
Þeah þe græf wille   golde stregan
broþor his geborenum,   byrgan be deadum,
maþmum mislicum   þæt hine mid wille,
ne mæg þære sawle   þe biþ synna ful
gold to geoce   for godes egsan,
þonne he hit ær hydeð   þenden he her leofað.

Micel biþ se meotudes egsa,   forþon hi seo molde oncyrreð;
se gestaþelade   stiþe grundas,
eorþan sceatas   ond uprodor.
Dol biþ se þe him his dryhten ne ondrædeþ;   cymeð him se deað
                                    unþinged.
Eadig bið se þe eaþmod leofaþ;   cymeð him seo ar of heofonum.
Meotod him þæt mod gestaþelað,   forþon he in his meahte gelyfeð.
Stieran mon sceal strongum mode,   ond þæt on staþelum healdan,
ond gewis werum,   wisum clæne,
scyle monna gehwylc   mid gemete healdan
wiþ leofne ond wið laþne   bealo,
þeah þe he hine wille fyres   fulne
oþþe on bæle   forbærnedne
his geworhtne wine.   Wyrd biþ swiþre,
meotud meahtigra   þonne ænges monnes gehygd.

Uton we hycgan   hwær we ham agen,
ond þonne geþencan   hu we þider cumen,

the hands will stop stirring and the mind from turning.
Though a sibling might wish to scatter
gold on the grave of his brother,
heap up by his side all the treasures he chose to take with him,
the silver he stashed while he lived
will be little comfort to that sin-stained soul
when it faces God's fury.

Great is Architect's awe, from which the world flinches,
he who set out the solid seabed
and the soaring sky, every inch of the earth.
Only a fool doesn't fear the Lord: death will give him no warning.
Blessed is he who lives humbly: heaven's honour will be his.
God establishes the mind in his people because he believes in
    its power.
A man must hold down a headstrong spirit, fix it in firm foundations,
be straight in his dealings and true in his motives,
have proportion and poise,
both in the loathing of rivals and love of allies –
wish as he might the heat of hell's fire
on his foe and the flame of the pyre
for his friend. The forces of fate
(God's greatness), are more than we mortals can grasp.

So let us consider where we might have a home
and reflect upon how we might get there,

ond we þonne eac tilien, þæt we to moten
in þa ecan   eadignesse,
þær is lif gelong   in lufan dryhtnes,
hyht in heofonum.   Þæs sy þam halgan þonc,
þæt he usic geweorþade,   wuldres ealdor,
ece dryhten,   in ealle tid.   Amen.

haul away in the hope of arriving
in the port of perpetual pleasure,
where there's life to be lived in the love of a Lord,
hope in the heavens. Thanks be to God,
Prince of Glory, for the grace he has granted,
Lord everlasting, through all time. Amen.

THE WHALE

Nu ic fitte gen   ymb fisca cynn
wille woðcræfte   wordum cyþan
þurh modgemynd   bi þam miclan hwale.

Se bið unwillum   oft gemeted,
frecne ond ferðgrim,   fareðlacendum,
niþþa gehwylcum;   þam is noma cenned,
fyrnstreama geflotan,   Fastitocalon.
Is þæs hiw gelic   hreofum stane,
swylce worie   bi wædes ofre,
sondbeorgum ymbseald,   særyrica mæst,
swa þæt wenaþ   wægliþende
þæt hy on ealond sum   eagum wliten,
ond þonne gehydað   heahstefn scipu
to þam unlonde   oncyrrapum,
setlaþ sæmearas   sundes æt ende,
ond þonne in þæt eglond   up gewitað
collenferþe;   ceolas stondað
bi staþe fæste,   streame biwunden.
Ðonne gewiciað   werigferðe,
faroðlacende,   frecnes ne wenað,

THE WHALE

Next up is a song on a species of fish,
put into words with the power of poetry:
a show of my wit on the might of the whale.

Hostile and hell-bent on harm,
seafarers rarely seek this one by choice.
Men call him the Old Current Crawler
('Fastitocalon' if you're fastidious).
His skin has the look of the crumbling shale
that flakes at the fringe of the ocean.
Always the sturdiest bar on the sandbank,
he invites the sailors' mistake:
faith in the eyes that spotted the Isle.
Mariners moor ships to the mirage,
tall bows fixed with anchor and rope,
settle their steeds at edge of the strand,
and haul themselves up on the high ground
with pride in their hearts. Keels keep
watch at the shore, waves winding between them.
The sailors are spent, set up their camp –
not sensing the threat, they summon a flame:

on þam ealonde   æled weccað,
heahfyr ælað;   hæleþ beoþ on wynnum,
reonigmode,   ræste geliste.

    Þonne gefeleð   facnes cræftig
þæt him þa ferend on   fæste wuniaþ,
wic weardiað   wedres on luste,
ðonne semninga   on sealtne wæg
mid þa noþe   niþer gewiteþ
garsecges gæst,   grund geseceð,
ond þonne in deaðsele   drence bifæsteð
scipu mid scealcum.   Swa bið scinna þeaw,
deofla wise,   þæt hi drohtende
þurh dyrne meaht   duguðe beswicað,
ond on teosu tyhtaþ   tilra dæda,
wemað on willan,   þæt hy wraþe secen,
frofre to feondum,   oþþæt hy fæste ðær
æt þam wærlogan   wic geceosað.

    Þonne þæt gecnaweð   of cwicsusle
flah feond gemah,   þætte fira gehwylc
hæleþa cynnes   on his hringe biþ
fæste gefeged,   he him feorgbona
þurh sliþen searo   siþþan weorþeð,
wloncum ond heanum,   þe his willan her
firenum fremmað,   mid þam he færinga,
heoloþhelme biþeaht,   helle seceð,

big bonfires make for happy heroes,
bone-tired and ready for bed.

Skilled at the sting, he awaits the sensation
that the seamen are safely ensconced,
keeping camp while they watch for fair weather.
Then all of a sudden, he surges in style,
our sea-spectre, taking them down
on the salt-way. Bottom bound,
it's one last drink in the death hall
for the ships and their crew. Such is the custom
of demons, the downtime of devils:
conning mankind with their cunning conceits,
teasing out wrong things from right,
warping men's minds so that swiftly they seek
comfort from captors, before choosing
a more permanent place in the truth-twister's tribe.

From the moment the feckless fiend senses (trapped in
      his torment)
that a member of mankind is snagged in his noose,
he sets out to slay them with the cruellest contrivance:
the vain and vicious — all the shameless purveyors of
      his sham.
Without any warning, the Prince of Heartlessness
puts on his Helmet of Hiding, plots a heading for hell,

goda geasne, grundleasne wylm
under mistglome, swa se micla hwæl,
se þe bisenceð sæliþende
eorlas ond yðmearas. He hafað oþre gecynd,
wæterþisa wlonc, wrætlicran gien.

Þonne hine on holme hungor bysgað
ond þone aglæcan ætes lysteþ,
ðonne se mereweard muð ontyneð,
wide weleras; cymeð wynsum stenc
of his innoþe, þætte oþre þurh þone,
sæfisca cynn, beswicen weorðaþ,
swimmað sundhwate þær se sweta stenc
ut gewiteð. Hi þær in farað
unware weorude, oþþæt se wida ceafl
gefylled bið; þonne færinga
ymbe þa herehuþe hlemmeð togædre
grimme goman. Swa biþ gumena gehwam,
se þe oftost his unwærlice
on þas lænan tid lif bisceawað,
læteð hine beswican þurh swetne stenc,
leasne willan, þæt he biþ leahtrum fah
wið wuldorcyning. Him se awyrgda ongean
æfter hinsiþe helle ontyneð,
þam þe leaslice lices wynne
ofer ferhtgereaht fremedon on unræd.

and sucks them into a bottomless bubbling of nebulous
    blackness –
much like our mighty whale; the sinker of sailors,
warriors on water-ponies. More wondrous still
is a second skill attached to this superb swimmer:

Fixated on food as he floats on the flood,
a monster with a longing for lunch,
the mere-warder opens his mouth
(luscious lips) and lets out from his innards
a pleasing perfume – of the type that
fools other families of fish. Straight for that sweet fragrance
the swift-swimmers head. Inside they sally,
this blithe band of brothers, until the great gob is full to
    the groaning.
Then all of a sudden, with the spoils surrounded,
the mighty mandible clangs closed. In much the same way
    (one might say)
so it goes for the man who moves through his life
in this transitory time with a lack of attention.
Too easily persuaded by that most pleasing perfume,
Worldly Pleasure, he soon finds himself guilty of wrongs:
sins against splendorous God. For him and his sort
Satan opens up Hell, drawing them in after death:
all the fools and the dupes who held fleshly delights
to be dearer than the dues of the soul.

Þonne se fæcna   in þam fæstenne
gebroht hafað,   bealwes cræftig,
æt þam edwylme   þa þe him on cleofiað,
gyltum gehrodene,   ond ær georne his
in hira lifdagum   larum hyrdon,
þonne he þa grimman   goman bihlemmeð
æfter feorhcwale   fæste togædre,
helle hlinduru;   nagon hwyrft ne swice,
utsiþ æfre,   þa þær in cumað,
þon ma þe þa fiscas   faraðlacende
of þæs hwæles fenge   hweorfan motan.
Forþon is eallinga
dryhtna dryhtne,   ond a deoflum wiðsace
wordum ond weorcum,   þæt we wuldorcyning
geseon moton.   Uton a sibbe to him
on þas hwilnan tid   hælu secan,
þæt we mid swa leofne   in lofe motan
to widan feore   wuldres neotan.

Skilled at destruction, the deceiver next
chivvies them into that chamber,
those who cling to him covered with sins,
who lapped up his lore all the days of their lives.
It's then that the conman clangs closed
Hell's hateful jaws, the Portcullis of Pain,
on the terminally toasted. Once over that threshold
there's no means of escape, no 'excuse me' or exit,
any more than there is for the seafaring fish
when he wishes to wheel from the chomp of the whale.
Such is the way of the world . . .
Lord of Lords. Let us always deny then these devils
with our words and our works, in order that one day
     we'll witness
God in his Glory. And let us look to him always
for peace and protection as we pass through our lives,
so that in glory with our Beloved
we may ever more bask in his brilliance.

WULF AND EADWACER

Leodum is minum   swylce him mon lac gife.
Willað hy hine aþecgan,   gif he on þreat cymeð.
Ungelic is us.
Wulf is on iege,   ic on oþerre.
Fæst is þæt eglond,   fenne biworpen.
Sindon wælreowe   weras þær on ige;
Willað hy hine aþecgan,   gif he on þreat cymeð.
Ungelice is us.
Wulfes ic mines widlastum   wenum dogode;
þonne hit wæs renig weder   ond ic reotugu sæt,
þonne mec se beaducafa   bogum bilegde,
wæs me wyn to þon,   wæs me hwæþre eac lað.
Wulf, min Wulf,   wena me þine
seoce gedydon,   þine seldcymas,
murnende mod,   nales meteliste.
Gehyrest þu, Eadwacer?   Uncerne earne hwelp
bireð wulf to wuda.
Þæt mon eaþe tosliteð   þætte næfre gesomnad wæs,
uncer giedd geador.

WULF AND EADWACER

It's like he was sent as an offering to my folk.
They'll have him if he's caught in this crisis.
It's different for us:
Wulf is on one island, I'm on another.
His isle's remote, ringed by the black fens.
The men on the island mean murder;
they'll have him if he's caught by their troop:
they're different from us.
The sky cried and I wept with it,
imagining my Wulf on his wanderings,
his battle hardness upon me.
I found pleasure in that, and also pain.
Wulf, my Wolf, these illusions of you
made me ill; I can't eat
for your absence devours me.
Do you hear that, Eadwacer? Some wolf
carries our poor whelp to the willows.
Never truly tied, how easily it tears apart:
the riddle of us two together.

from THE PHOENIX

          Is þæt æþele lond
blostmum geblowen.   Beorgas þær ne muntas
steape ne stondað,   ne stanclifu
heah hlifiað,   swa her mid us,
ne dene ne dalu   ne dunscrafu,
hlæwas ne hlincas,   ne þær hleonað oo
unsmeþes wiht,   ac se æþela feld
wridað under wolcnum,   wynnum geblowen.

         Ðone wudu weardaþ   wundrum fæger
fugel feþrum strong,   se is fenix haten.
Þær se anhaga   eard bihealdeþ,
deormod drohtað;   næfre him deaþ sceþeð
on þam willwonge,   þenden woruld stondeþ.

þær se wilda fugel   in þam westenne
ofer heanne beam   hus getimbreð.

Wyrta wearmiað,   willsele stymeð
swetum swæccum,   þonne on swole byrneð
þurh fyres feng   fugel mid neste.

from THE PHOENIX (lines 20–7, 85–9, 201–2, 213–19, 240–2)

That illustrious land
is brimming with blossoms. No mountains or bluffs
climb steeply there; nor do rocky cliffs
loom high overhead like they do here.
You'll find neither coombs or hollows or gulleys,
barrows or boundary banks; no land that needs breaking
lies around. Instead, that peerless plain
thrives under the skies, thronged with joy.

A strong-winged bird of wondrous beauty
keeps charge in the forest: they call it the Phoenix.
The solitary creature sticks to its territory,
holds bravely to its way. As long as this world goes on,
death can never come near it . . .

There in the wilderness the wild
bird builds a house, high in a tree . . .

Perfumed plants warm up and the pleasant hall
exhales sweet scents. Then in the swelter
the bird and its nest burn in the fire's embrace.

Appendix

Bæl bið onæled.   Þonne brond þeceð
heorodreorges hus,   hreoh onetteð,
fealo lig feormað   ond fenix byrneð,
fyrngearum frod.

                    Þonne bræd weorþeð
eal edniwe   eft acenned,
synnum asundrad.

The funeral pyre ignites, the fire engulfing
the home of that sorry sacrifice. Savage, they hurry on –
pale flames feed and feast on the Phoenix,
a creature made wise by its countless years . . .

                        After that, the burned body
is wholly renewed and reborn,
shorn of its sins.

---

from THE WANDERER

Hwær cwom mearg?   Hwær cwom mago?   Hwær cwom
                              maþþumgyfa?
Hwær cwom symbla gesetu?   Hwær sindon seledreamas?
Eala beorht bune!   Eala byrnwiga!
Eala þeodnes þrym! Hu seo þrag gewat,
genap under nihthelm,   swa heo no wære.

from THE WANDERER (lines 92–6)

Where has the horse gone? Where has the man gone? Where have the
     treasure-givers gone?
Where are the seats at the feast? Where are the joys of the hall?
So long to the sparkling cup. So long to the warrior in wargear.
So long to princely power. See how that era has passed,
faded into nothingness under night's helmet, as if it had never been.

Acknowledgements

As instrumental to this book as the sources themselves, are the staff of the Department of Anglo-Saxon, Norse and Celtic, who, at the University of Cambridge, 2010 to 2012, introduced me to stories, objects and manuscripts, as well as ways of reading them, that have lent richness and vibrancy to my life ever since. Thank you all.

For enriching this book with their specialist expertise, I must thank: Chris Pig, Dan Matthews, Dr Kate Rundell, Dr Christina Faraday, Dana Weaver, Dr Mary Wellesley, Dr Jordan Pullicino, Philip Jeffs, Olive Crompton, Dr Anya Burgon, Dr Seán Hewitt, Professor Richard Dance and Dr George Younge.

Thanks also goes to all those at Quercus, who

embraced my proposal and sent it into the world, among them: Jon Butler, Jon Riley, Jasmine Palmer, Lipfon Tang, Ellie Nightingale, Ana Sampson and Elizabeth Masters. Likewise, I am as grateful as it is possible to be to Jasmine and Jon for editing my drafts with such benevolent brilliance and to Nick de Somogyi for his meticulous copy editing.

Another thanks is due to Jon Riley for alerting me to an episode of BBC Radio 4's *Desert Island Discs*, aired on Friday, 18 March 2022, in which Robert Plant, of Led Zeppelin fame, chose the Penguin edition of *The First Poems in English* for his desert island hermitage. I must thank Robert Plant for making this choice, which filled me with confidence while creating a book inspired by the same poetry.

I am furthermore grateful to the musicians behind the music created for the audiobook of *Wild*. Robbie Haylett, thank you for sharing your skill as arranger, composer and baritone. Stephen Wilkinson and Christina Riedl, thank you for singing beside him. Good and pleasant it is to be singing together in unity.

Acknowledgements

Chris Keelty and Will Rumney, thank you for swapping spars and chisels for bows and strings; all your work is beautiful.

A special thanks must go to Dr George Younge for translating a number of the Exeter Book poems afresh. I think you have captured the emotional power of these early verses with such compassion and skill. It is an honour to have my words printed alongside yours, for the sake of words that have shaped us both.

Finally this book could not have been written without the support, both practical and moral, of family. I would especially like to thank my husband, Will Rumney, for journeying alongside me in the research for this book, and for looking after our daughter if I happened to be sliding down underground passageways, or slipping through a reed bed.

AMY JEFFS

May Eve, 2022

Further Reading

One: Earth

As well as those provided by George Younge (see appendix), for translations of the Old English elegies and other poems, see S. A. J. Bradley's *Anglo-Saxon Poetry*, first published in 1982, as well as Elaine Treharne's *Old and Middle English, c.890-c.1450: An Anthology* (2000) and Michael Alexander's *The First Poems in English* (Penguin, 1966). Translations of *The Wife's Lament* are found in all three books, while *Guthlac A* can be found in Bradley.

For Bede's *On the Nature of Things*, see the annotated translation by Calvin B. Kendall and Faith Wallis (Liverpool University Press, 2010). For Isidore of Seville's *Etymologies*, see the translation by Stephen A. Barney, W. J. Lewis, J. A. Beach and Oliver Berghof (Cambridge University Press, 2006). References to Celtic myth are taken from James MacKillop's *Dictionary of Celtic Mythology* (Oxford University Press, 1998).

The Franks Casket is on display in Room 41 of the British Museum, and a helpful guide to its iconographies, inscriptions and context can be found in Leslie Webster's *The Franks Casket* (British Museum Press, 2012).

Further secondary reading relevant to this chapter include Sarah Semple's 'Fear of the Past: The Place of the Prehistoric Burial Mound in the Ideology of Middle and Later Anglo-Saxon England', *World Archaeology* 30, No. 1 (June 1998), pp. 109–126; and *Perceptions of the Prehistoric in Anglo-Saxon England: Religion, Ritual, and Rulership in the Landscape* (Oxford University Press, 2013). These publications make frequent use of the work of Andrew Reynolds, especially his *Anglo-Saxon Deviant Burial Customs* (Oxford University Press, 2009).

An overview of medieval perceptions of nature can be gained from Richard Jones' *The Medieval Natural World* (Routledge, 2013).

Two: Ocean

Translated excerpts of *The Wanderer* and the whole of *The Seafarer* provided by Younge (see appendix). See the translation of Isidore of Seville's *Etymologies* cited above. For Tacitus on *Germania*, see J. B. Rives' edition of Harold Mattingly's translation of *Agricola and Germania* (Penguin, 2010). Passing reference is made in this chapter to the corpus of Norse myths: translations of the primary sources include Carolyne Larrington's *The Poetic Edda* (second edition, Oxford University Press, 2014) and Jesse Byock's *The Prose Edda: Norse Mythology* (Penguin, 2005).

For further discussion of the themes of earthly transience in the Old English elegies, see *The Cambridge Companion to Old English Literature*, edited by Malcolm Godden and Michael Lapidge (Cambridge University Press, 1991), especially Chapter 10, 'Perceptions of Transience', by Christine Fell.

Three: Forest

A collection of translated examples of medieval Celtic nature poetry, including the *Claf Abercuawg*, *Buile Suibhne* (*The Madness of Sweeney*) and *The Song of Machín Laíth*, can be found in Kenneth Jackson's *Studies in Early Celtic Nature Poetry* (Cambridge University Press, 1935). For a more recent study of Welsh verse, see Jenny Rowland's *Early Welsh Saga Poetry: A Study and Edition of the 'Englynion'* (D. S. Brewer, 1990), from which I have taken the translation of *Claf Abercuawg*. In my discussion of Nebuchadnezzar, I refer to the Old Testament Book of Daniel and its Old English retelling, translated in Bradley's *Anglo-Saxon Poetry* (see above).

The story of the burning wildmen, or *Bal des Ardents*, can be found in the *Chroniques* of Froissart, and is explored in Barbara W. Tuchman's *A Distant Mirror: The Calamitous 14th Century* (Penguin, 1978).

My reference to Calcidius' use of the word *silva* derives from Anya Burgon's PhD thesis 'The Mechanical Arts and *Poiesis* in the Philosophy and Literature of the Twelfth-Century Schools' (Cambridge University, 2019) and Paul Binski's *Gothic Sculpture* (Yale University Press, 2019). See also *Calcidius on Plato's 'Timaeus': Greek Philosophy, Latin Reception, and Christian Contexts* by Gretchen Reydams-Schils (Cambridge University Press, 2020).

Seán Hewitt's verse retelling of the *Buile Suibhne* (*The Madness of Sweeney*) can be found in his debut collection, *Tongues of Fire* (Jonathan Cape, 2020).

Four: Beast

The Old English poem *The Whale* is one of three poems inspired by the second-century Greek text *The Physiologus*, which can be read in translation in Michael J. Curley's *Physiologus: A Medieval Book of Nature Lore* (University of Chicago Press, 2009). The whale's legendary ploy of posing as an island appears in all these texts, as well as in *Navigatio Sancti Brendani Abbatis* (*The Voyage of St Brendan the Abbot*), a translation of which, alongside other versions of this remarkable wonder tale, can be read in *The Voyage of St Brendan: Representative Versions of the Legend in English Translation*, edited by

W. R. J. Barron and Glyn S. Burgess (Liverpool University Press, 2002).

The story of Jonah and the whale (versions of which exist in many cultures) can be found in the Old Testament Book of Jonah, as well as the Gospels of Matthew (12: 38–41 and 16: 4) and Luke (11: 29–32). For information on the Franks Casket, see Leslie Webster's *The Franks Casket* (2012), visit the real object in Room 41 of the British Museum, or find zoomable images on the British Museum's online collection: https://www.britishmuseum.org/collection.

Five: Fen

Wulf and Eadwacer is given in translation by Younge (see appendix). Select translations of the Old English Exeter Book riddles can be found in Treharne and Bradley (see further reading for Chapter One). The Exeter Book's shelf-mark is Exeter Cathedral Library MS 3501.

It is worth consuming these amazing, enigmatic works of literature alongside images of contemporary art. The Sutton Hoo ship burial treasures can be seen in real life in Room 41 of the British Museum. Gareth Williams' 2011 *Treasure from Sutton Hoo* contains high resolution colour images of the treasures, as does the British Museum's online collection.

For a general discussion of the theme of nature in this body of literature, see Jennifer Neville's *Representations of the Natural World in Old English Poetry* (Cambridge University Press, 1999). For a recent, lavishly illustrated overview of the English art of this period, see the British Library's exhibition catalogue *Anglo-Saxon Kingdoms: Art, Word, War*, edited by Claire Breay and Joanna Story (2018). For Celtic art, see *Work of Angels: Masterpieces of Celtic Metalwork, 6th–9th Centuries AD*, edited by Susan Youngs (British Museum Press, 1989), and the exhibition catalogue for the British Museum's *Celts: Art and Identity*, edited by Julia Farley and Fraser Hunter (2015).

Six: Catastrophe

An excerpt of the Old English poem *Judgement Day II*, preserved in the Parker Library, Corpus Christi College, Cambridge, MS 201, is provided in translation by Younge. For the birds singing Psalm 133, see *The Voyage of St Brendan: Representative Versions of the Legend in English Translation*, ed. Barron and Burgess (see above). To scrutinise the imagery of the Lindisfarne Gospels (Cotton MS Nero D IV), visit the digital facsimile on the British Library's 'Digitised Manuscripts' resource: http://www.bl.uk/manuscripts/Full Display.aspx?ref=cotton_ms_nero_d_iv. A single opening is generally on display in the Treasure Gallery of the British Library. More details of the technical analysis of pigments and decoration can be found in a British Library Collection

Care blogpost from 29 July 2013: 'Under the microscope with the Lindisfarne Gospels'.

The entry for the 793 sacking of Lindisfarne has been translated by Michael Swanton in *The Anglo-Saxon Chronicles* (Phoenix Press, 2000). Both this account and Alcuin's letter to the Bishop of Lindisfarne – a full translation of which can be found in *English Historical Documents I: c. 500–1142*, edited by Dorothy Whitelock (second edition, Oxford University Press, 1979) – are discussed in Charles C. Rozier's *Writing History in the Community of St Cuthbert, c. 700–1130: From Bede to Symeon of Durham* (Boydell Press, 2020). I note the letter's similarity in tone to Gildas' *The Ruin of Britain*, which has been translated by Michael Winterbottom (Phillimore, 1978).

Alcuin's letters, especially their homoerotic undertones, have been subject to much discussion. In *Who's Who in Gay and Lesbian History: From Antiquity to World War II*, edited by Robert Aldrich and Garry Wotherspoon (Routledge, 2001), David Bromwell offers excerpts of his letters in translation. A comprehensive translation of his letters can be found in Stephen Allott's *Alcuin of York, ca. AD 732 to 804: His Life and Letters* (William Sessions, 1974).

To better understand the philosophical background to all the medieval sources discussed in this book, but particularly in relation to the theme of disaster, see Peter Walsh's translation of Boethius' *The Consolation of Philosophy* (Oxford University Press, 1999).

Seven: Paradise

My final chapter uses as its primary sources the Old English poems *The Phoenix*, *The Panther* and *The Husband's Message*, an excerpt from the first of which has been provided by Younge (see appendix). The latter pair have been translated by Treharne and Bradley respectively (see further reading for Chapter One). In addition to Isidore of Seville's *Etymologies*, translated by Barney, Lewis and Beach (see above), an excerpt from Treharne's translation of 'The Husband's Message' is also cited, as well as portions of Riddle 12.). The seven-year journey to the same wondrous islands and, ultimately, an earthly paradise, derives from *The Voyage of St Brendan the Abbot*, translated by Barron and Burgess.

Further reading pertinent to this chapter can be found in *The Otherworld Voyage in Early Irish Literature: An Anthology of Criticism*, edited by Jonathan M. Wooding (Four Courts Press, 2014), and Jane Hawkes and Susan Mills' edited volume *Northumbria's Golden Age* (Sutton Press, 1999). A general overview of the period and place covered by this book is offered in Rory Naismith's *Early Medieval Britain, c. 500–1000* (Cambridge University Press, 2021).

I hope that this book has offered its reader an absorbing journey, an introduction to a fascinating subject, and a demonstration that, when it comes to cultures shaped by migration, exchange, invasion and faith, not even islands are islands.

Index

Index

Index

Index

Index